K

DATE DUE

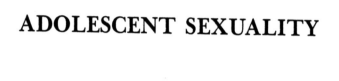

ADOLESCENT SEXUALITY

ADOLESCENT SEXUALITY

By

JULES H. MASSERMAN, M.D.

*Professor and Co-Chairman Emeritus
of Psychiatry and Neurology
Northwestern University, Chicago
Past President
American Psychiatric Association*

and

VICTOR M. URIBE, M.D.

*Assistant Professor of Psychiatry
Northwestern University and Loyola
University, Chicago*

CHARLES C THOMAS • PUBLISHER
Springfield • Illinois • U.S.A.

Published and Distributed Throughout the World by

CHARLES C THOMAS • PUBLISHER
2600 South First Street
Springfield, Illinois 62794-9265

© *1989 by* CHARLES C THOMAS • PUBLISHER
ISBN 0-398-05629-3
Library of Congress Catalog Card Number:89-37631

With THOMAS BOOKS *careful attention is given to all details of manufacturing
and design. It is the Publisher's desire to present books that are satisfactory as to their
physical qualities and artistic possibilities and appropriate for their particular use.*
THOMAS BOOKS *will be true to those laws of quality that assure a good name
and good will.*

Printed in the United States of America
SC-R-3

Library of Congress Cataloging-in-Publication Data

Masserman, Jules Hymen, 1905-
    Adolescent sexuality / by Jules H. Masserman and Victor M. Uribe.
        p.   cm.
    Includes bibliographical references.
    ISBN 0-398-05629-3
    1. Psychosexual disorders in adolescence.   2. Teenage sex
offenders—Mental health.   3. Teenagers—Sexual behavior.
4. Adolescent psychiatry.   I. Uribe, Victor M.   II. Title.
RJ506.P72M37   1989
616.85'83'0083—dc20   89-37631
                                                                            CIP

To
Christine
and to
Martha and Sonia

FOREWORD

The understanding of adolescent behavior represents a major concern for parents and others who live with, or are responsible for adolescent lives. The authors of this text have made this complex relationship clear for those of us who love our children and wish to be an integral part of their future. With warmth and a precise knowledge of the primal roots of human development and an erudite grasp of anthropology, anatomy, physiology, and sociology, they have used their psychiatric training and experience to produce this expert guide to adolescent conduct, and have woven current scientific theories and research developments into an eminently readable book.

One must wonder at the literary capacities demonstrated in producing this lucid exposition of the complexities, pains, and achievements of teenage sexuality. We have observed the influence of our youth on our industries, on our arts, and on every aspect of our culture, and have observed successful or failed developments of adolescence projected into adulthood. This book is a welcome guide for those who wish our youth health, success, and happiness, and a salutory influence on our society.

HAROLD M. VISOTSKY, M.D.
Professor and Chairman
Institute of Psychiatry
Northwestern University

PREFACE

Many thoughtful observers accept the early expressions of sexuality in the present generation of adolescents as desirable seekings for openness, empathy, and companionship, and as preparations for the enduring devotions of marriage and parenthood—foundations of a progressive social and cultural order. However, when complicated by familial instabilities, economic deprivations, educational deficiencies, cultural confusions, and other stresses, adolescent sexuality is increasingly associated with somatic dysfunctions, delinquency, addictions to alcohol and drugs, venereal disease, pregnancy, abortion or premature motherhood, abuse of unwanted children, suicide, and other serious impairments of individual and social welfare.

With what the authors hope is lucidity and brevity, this book traces the genetic, developmental, and sociocultural determinants of sexuality from conception to adolescence, and presents the effective treatment of its deviations as evolved during decades of research, teaching, and clinical experience.

The case illustrations are clinically valid composites of sources of referral, techniques of examination, diagnostic inferences, modes of therapy, and follow-up results; however, in no instance do they specify individual patients.

The book is dedicated to the welfare of our youth, and thereby of our future.

J.H.M.
V.M.U.

CONTENTS

CASE ILLUSTRATIONS

INDIVIDUAL AND FAMILY THERAPIES

PEER REVIEWS

FORENSIC CONSULTATIONS

ADOLESCENT SEXUALITY

Chapter 1

THE ORIGINS OF SEXUALITY

Ten (or 20?) billions of years ago, a Primal Source of Infinite Energy (God?) released countless quadrillions of stars to illuminate the universe with nuclear brilliance before fading into mystic black holes and being resurrected in an eternal Cycle of Creation. Five (or 10?) billions of years later, trillions of these stars formed a celestial spiral we call "our" Milky Way, in one arm of which there appeared a small incandescent sphere we call "our" sun. Out of the primal clouds surrounding it nine (?) orbiting planets formed, the third-nearest being "our" Earth. As it, too, cooled, its wave-particles coalesced, first into atoms of hydrogen (one electron circling one proton), then helium (two of each), and progressively into a multiplicity of complex compounds.

Among those containing carbon there evolved megamolecules peculiarly capable of absorbing ("feeding on") surrounding atoms, growing and then duplicating (cloning) themselves, thus acquiring the characteristics of self-sustaining life. Some of these compounds, through mutual atomic attractions, began to unite with others to form more enduring combinations which in turn became capable of growth, division, and the generation of repeated unions among their offspring. In effect, this prototype of binary sexual reproduction[1] made possible the evolution of progressively more adaptable organisms, ranging from single-cell amoebae (which employ both cloning and genetic interchange), to the variegated multibillion-celled creatures that now share "our" environment.

HUMAN PROCREATION

The sexuality that so emerged in the earth's primeval waters is still synchronized in human beings with lunar high tides. About every 28 days, a neural center (the hypothalamus) deep in every woman's brain commands a nearby master endocrine gland (the pituitary) to secrete special metabolic regulators (hormones) into her blood stream. These chemical messengers cause one of her ovaries to release a sex cell (oocyte) into a uterine conduit (Fallopian tube) where, after a genetic reorganization (see below), it becomes a female progenitor (ovum) ready to meet and combine with a corresponding male cell (sperm) that had been deposited in her vagina. The resultant fertilized human egg (zygote) then proceeds to her womb (uterus), develops into an embryo and after nine months is born as a human being, the product of three billion (?) years of creative evolution.[2]

Female Component

How personal traits are transmitted from parents to offspring through chromosomes (carriers of DNA spirals called genes) is equally wondrous. In essence, the mother's physical features are determined by 22 pairs of differently constituted living matter (somatosomal chromosomes) in each of her cells, plus two sex (XX) chromosomes that made her female. However, on its way to the uterus the oocyte, which at first contained all 46 chromosomes, had divided into one large and one small "daughter" cell (a process called meiosis) so that each has only 22 unpaired somatosomes and only a single X (female) chromosome. The smaller cell then fades away, and only the larger one (the ovum) is propelled through the Fallopian tube toward the uterus, to be fertilized[3] enroute either by a female (X) or a male (Y) sperm.

Concurrently, both ovaries expand into glands (corpora lutea) that, together with the pituitary and adrenals (endocrine glands above each kidney), secrete special hormones (progesterones) that thicken the lining of the uterus into a nourishing tissue (endometrium) richly supplied with blood vessels to sustain the developing zygote. However, if the ovum is not fertilized, progesterone levels decrease and the endometrium is expelled by menstruation, followed by a 10-day "safe period" until the next oocyte is released. Nor can pregnancy occur if special hormone combinations taken in contraceptive pills interfere with normal monthly estrogen-progesterone (sex-stimulating *vs.* gestation) cycles.

Male Components

Every cell in a human male also contains 22 pairs of somatosomal chromosomes that determine his physical features, whereas each of the 23rd pairs is an XY sex chromosome that made him male. The millions of mobile gametes produced by his testicles also contain this full set of 46 chromosomes, but when they, too, split by meiosis, half the resulting sperm have only the single X (female) chromosome, and the other half only the male Y. All the sperm are then nourished in a testicular appendage called the epididymis until they are ejaculated in the seminal fluid during orgasm.

Impregnation

The millions of sperm cells deposited in the vagina during ejaculation immediately use their whip-like tails to swim through the entrance to the uterus (cervix) and up the Fallopian tubes at a speed of about an eighth of an inch a minute. When the swiftest cell meets the ovum, sperm and ovum unite to form a human seed (zygote) with a full complement of 46 chromosomes. Sex is then also determined: if by slightly better than even chance the penetrating sperm carries a single X chromosome to pair with the ovum's single X the resultant pre-embryonic zygote will be an XX female; if the successful sperm carries a Y, the embryo will be an XY male.[4] However, the following variations may occur.

Multiple Births

Once in about every 86 pregnancies (more often in some families) two ova are simultaneously released and both are fertilized by separate sperms. Dizygotic twins, often of similar physical characteristics but of the same or opposite sex, are then born and may develop similar or different personality traits.

Once in about 250 pregnancies a single fertilized ovum divides into two or, much less frequently, into several viable zygotes, each of which can be separately nurtured in the uterus and be born as monozygotic siblings with identical hereditary characteristics.

Somatic Abnormalities

Once in 400 or 500 pregnancies, especially in older women, the ovum after meiosis retains an extra somatosome, resulting in "trisomy" at locus 21 on its genetic helix. The embryo may then survive as a *Down's syndrome* (misnamed "mongoloid") infant, physically, sexually, and mentally handicapped, but usually capable of a gentle, affectionate disposition if correspondingly treated. Childhood *autisms* (impenetrable self-preoccupations, peculiar obsessions, and irrational reactions to stimuli) and *Tourette's syndrome* (barking speech, motor incoordination, convulsive tendencies, tics, and hyperactivity) may also be congenital. Somato-somal abnormalities may likewise predispose to cystic fibrosis, diabetes, metabolic and neural dysfunctions, and various hereditary disorders not yet traced to specific genes.

The development of a normal zygote may also be seriously impaired by the mother's emotional disturbances and attendant hormonal imbalances, her intake of toxic drugs[5] or her addictions to alcohol, tobacco, cocaine, or opiates, or by maternal hemophilia, diabetes, toxoplasmosis, or inter-current illness.

Sexual Abnormalities

In rare instances, failures in sex-cell exchanges during meiosis or mitosis (chromosomal divisions) may leave the zygote with only one X chromosome. The resulting XO embryo appears feminine, but does not secrete estrogens, and after birth does not develop full femininity or fertility (*Turner's syndrome*).

Other deviations in X or Y distributions may produce an XXY embryo which, depending on the mother's intrauterine hormonal balance and especially on the child's preferential upbringing, develops either into a par-tially masculinized "female" (*Noonan's syndrome*)[6], or else into a eunuchoid "male" (*Klinefelter's syndrome*) with small testes, large breasts, weak libido, tendencies to transvestism, and other deviant physical and personality characteristics. Alternatively, an XYY male may be born with tendencies toward aggressivity, hypererotism, and resultant social maladaptations.

Extrauterine

Finally, any zygote may be impeded on its way to the uterus and begin to grow in the Fallopian tube as an ectopic pregnancy, destined either to die spontaneously or to burst the tube and be removed surgically.

UTERINE DEVELOPMENT

Fortunately for the human race, all such deviations are relatively infrequent, and the normally fertilized XX or XY zygote, still micro-scopic in size proceeds to its uterine haven, where it rapidly develops an extension (the placenta) into the endometrium from which it extracts rich nourishment. The growing embryo then recapitulates animate evo-lution by successively developing gills like a fish, then a tail and a reptilian urogenital sac (cloaca), then lateral eyes and a nasal snout similar to those in four-footed mammals and, after 20 weeks, a large brain and a recognizable human form. Again miraculously, within ten lunar months the embryo is prepared for the hazards and joys of extrauterine life.

ENDNOTES

1. Cloning is still represented by viruses: as a relatively simple example, an infectious crystalline compound called the tobacco virus absorbs atoms from tobacco leaves, comes "alive" and progressively reproduces itself.

2. This model of reproduction evolved from the first release of sex cells into primeval waters for chance survival of the young, through reptiles and birds that copulate and protect their eggs, to mammals that nourish their young internally and then provide them with complex and enduring postnatal care. (Plants employ winds and animals to carry their gametes from parent to parent and then to mother earth for nourishment.)

3. Since unfertilized ova usually die within a day, ardent pro-life advocates could also contend that every ovum deserves to have its life preserved by fertilization — though what to do with the billions of unsuccessful sperms fated to perish externally or intravaginally remains problematical.

4. Ashley Montagu commented to one of us(JHM), "Man is the only 150-pound computerized servomechanism that can be produced by unskilled labor." But even apart from its parents' skills, each child can claim to have been specially selected from the predestined union of only one among hundreds of its mother's ova and only one among billions of its father's sperm.

5. Thalidomide, a "nerve sedative" readily available for a time, caused thousands of fetal deformities before it was legally banned.

6. Exemplified by a medalist in the 1984 Women's Olympics. Rare XXX "super-females" have been reported as preferring erotic to athletic pursuits.

RECOMMENDED READING

Hawkins, S.W.: *A Brief History of Time.* New York, Bantam Books, 1988.

Jastrow, P.: *God and the Astronomers.* New York, W.W. Norton, 1978.

Miller, J.C. *Living Systems.* New York: McGraw-Hill, 1978.

Sadock, Virginia: Sexual Anatomy. Endocrinology and Physiology. In Kaplan, H., Freedman, A.M. and Sadock, B.J.: *Textbook of Psychiatry.* Baltimore, Williams and Williams, 1983, pp. 1667–1669.

Stoller, R.J.: *Masculinity and Femininity.* New York, Science House, 1968.

Thomas, L.: *The Lives of a Cell.* New York, Bantam Books, 1981.

Chapter 2

CHILDHOOD SEXUALITY

As indicated in Chapter 1, it is not until the fourth month of embryonic life that bisexual tissues appear, and differentiate either into ovaries if the fetus is an XX female, or testicles if an XY male. These glands correspondingly secrete hormones that differentially determine the development of either female or male external genitalia which soon become sites of pleasurable sensations since, as may be observed by ultrasound, 20-week embryos repeatedly manipulate them. Thus, all precursors of human sexuality—genetic coding, maternal symbiosis, embryonic development, bisexual potentialities, hormonal determinants of somatic form and function, and self-erotism—have been preordained even before birth introduces sociocultural influences.

FREUDIAN CONCEPTS OF POSTNATAL SEXUALITY

Although Sigmund Freud never directly analyzed a child, he inferred, from the retrospective "free associations" and fantasies of his adult patients, that during their childhood each had passed through a succession of (narcissistic, oral, anal, and phallic) "libidinal phases" which unconsciously continued to motivate all their later behavior.[1]

Freud's pervasive concepts of pansexuality will be here reviewed in a more comprehensive context.

Touch

Freud did not consider that the neonate's first dealings with the outside world—its delivery by obstetrician or midwife, its cleaning and bundling, its fondling by its mother or a surrogate—were tactile rather than "narcissistic." Yet these initial experiences, however inchoate and unformulated, continue to imbue with profound meaning all later interpersonal contacts, from a casual handshake to the "touching" relationships and attendant caresses of love; indeed, "feelings" would often take precedence over intellectual considerations in determining conduct. Conversely, children deprived of tender tactile "bonding," as often occurs in orphan or foster homes, may grow into self-isolated and misanthropic adults.

Vision

Next, the neonate opens its eyes, and ever afterwards, will equate "seeing" with perception, "illumination" with knowledge, "insight" with comprehension, and "vision" with imagination.

Spirituality

Freud also overlooked the significance of the neonate's first somatic response to its new world: its inhalation of air (Latin—*spiritus,* breath of life).[2] Again symbolically, the child will be raised in accord with various concepts of *spirituality;* it will join family and society in an *esprit de corps,* and be *inspired* toward special accomplishments. It will be taught that sexuality, too, should be *spiritual,* with marriage and progeny legitimized in the immanent presence of a deified Holy Spirit.[3] Conversely, failures in life will be *dispiriting* or *desperate,* modified only by a hope that death itself may be only an *expiration* —i.e., the release from travail of a *spirit* (soul) which will either be reborn in another body or remain elsewhere immortal.

Narcissism

This Freudian term, for the first phase of childhood "psychosexual" development, is derived from the Greek legend of the youth Narcissus who remained so intrigued with his own image reflected in a pond as to exclude all other relationships.[4] Freud then characterized the neonate as *polymorphous perverse,* "polymorphous" indicating a potentiality for developing diverse "cathexes" (relationships) with others, "perverse" connoting that these could be deviant as outlined below.

Orality

Freud inferred that the infant's emergence from narcissism occurs when it first suckles and then, during weaning, grasps, bites, and so attempts to retain the mother's breast. The following considerations apply to these subphases of libidinal orality respectively termed "incorporative" and "aggressive."

Embryonic

A four-month-old fetus, still "suckling" its mother through the placenta, can also be ultrasonically observed putting its budding thumb into its mouth, indicating the oral region as a pregenital site of sensory self-satisfaction. Postnatally, infants will contentedly suck on a pacifier, toddlers will utilize their thumbs, and adults will substitute unlit cigarettes, cigars, or pipes.[5] Conversely, compulsive gorging of food (bulimia) or over-reactive self-starvation (anorexia nervosa) may seriously impair sexuality.

Dependent Orality

At about the age of four months the infant will identify its mother and other caretakers as separate beings, and its later needs to be sustained by family, peers, spouse, and society will motivate reciprocal services. However, if the child is too greatly indulged, it may continue to be paralyzingly passive and culturally undeveloped into adulthood.

Libidinal Orality

Lovers are called "honey" or "sweetheart," nubile girls are "luscious," etc. Erotically, adolescents explore lingual and mammary contacts, and fellatio and cunnilingus may be preferred to genital intercourse.

Aggressive Orality

Conversely, if dependency needs are too early and too traumatically frustrated, the child may resort to attention-demanding tantrums, the adolescent to acquisitive delinquencies, and the adult either to compulsive seekings for wealth and power, or to vengefully acquisitive criminality— each with erotic projections.

Excretion

Freud considered the expulsion of metabolic products as also libidinal, and proposed that after orality, the child enters into "anal retentive" and "anal aggressive" phases of psychosexual development. Toddlers do show delight in urinating, defecating, spreading, and playing with their excrement; however, because many Western parents regard this as maintaining infantilism, they begin toilet training even before the infant is physiologically able to control its sphincters, usually at about the age of 18 months. Such discipline can be highly traumatic to the little prince or princess, to whom its parents had acted as servants rather than taskmasters in its previously subservient universe. The child may then respond with ambivalent compromises it will apply to other social problems throughout life. Examples:

In conformity, it accedes to the use of the potty, cleansing tissues, and delayed access to the toilet, after which, in adolescence it may proceed to obsessive cleanliness and, in adulthood, to compulsive rituals, religious scrupulosity, and reciprocal tyrannies over offspring.

Conversely, the resentful youngster may litter, deface, or vandalize the environment and, in adulthood, repeat "dirty" jokes and stories, indulge in the supposedly beneficial effects of mud baths, and prefer scatologic sex practices such as sodomy.

Phallic Phase

Freud also inferred that between the ages of four and six, little boys, in response to penile erections and orgasms, become proud of their phalluses, whereas little girls feel "castrated," suffer from "penis envy," and ever afterward accept physical, intellectual, moral, and esthetic subservience to males. Fortunately, this assignment of sexual roles is rarely practiced by mutually respectful parents in most culturally ecletic Western families; nor is gender *inferiority* spontaneously adopted by their offspring. Clitoris and phallus continue to be sources of pleasurable sensations in both sexes. Toddlers examine their differing genitalia with similar interest and soon differentiate their genders with equal pride in related behavioral patterns. Little girls choose pink dresses and want bows in their hair, prefer dolls and household toys, and accompany mothers to public toilets; little boys wear pants, prefer mechanical and mobile gifts, and play appropriate roles in mommy-and-daddy and doctor-and-nurse games, often with mutual sexual explorations.

However, since many parents discourage more direct manifestations of early erotism, pudendal displays are frowned upon, innocently repeated erotic words are hushed, bathing is sexually segregated, and parental intercourse pointedly hidden. As a result, the child may regard his or her spontaneous sexuality as forbidden, and respond with another set of ambivalent behaviors that later become pronounced in adolescence and pervasive in adulthood. Examples:

In disciplined compliance, sex organs must ever be concealed; ejaculations and menstrual flows equated with other excreta as "soiling"; kissing or other oral displays of affection, even between married couples, are regressively "in bad taste," and sexual intercourse must be secretive and, in some religions, exclusively procreative.

In rebellion, clothes may approach nudity on stages and beaches; huggings are increasingly acceptable as social greetings; sexual promiscuity is covertly condoned, holiday sexual orgies may transcend everyday bounds, and pornography and prostitution persist as ancient cultural institutions.

Latent Period

Freud thought that after this preliminary "phallic" phase from four to six years, sexuality subsides until puberty. Some analysts retain this concept, although every parent can observe differential prepubertal sex-related expressions to the contrary. Girls emphasize their femininity with short, attractive dresses, special hair styles, winsome graces, and miniatured coquettery, anticipate domesticity by learning sewing and crocheting, and practice maternity in caring for pets and younger siblings. Boys prepare for adult roles by greater interests in mechanical constructions and mobile vehicles (skateboards, bicycles), and develop physical strength through athletics and competitive skills in group games. Girls take up musical instruments that respond best to gentle manipulation (piano, violin, viola, cello), whereas boys may prefer woodwinds (oboe, clarinet) or brass (saxophone, horns) that trumpet a more virile voice, while both sexes use Rock 'n' Roll and other erotic music as equal stimulants to sexuality.[6]

Prepubertal girls become correspondingly conscious of their body image, wear bras even before detectable breast development, explore individual or mutual clitoral masturbation and, in many instances, encourage sexual fondling and genital contacts within or outside the family (Case 1). Prepubertal boys write, draw, and collect pornography, masturbate frequently, indulge in phallic exhibitions (Case 12), and proceed as far toward homo- or heterosexual contacts as opportunities afford.[7]

Characterologic Derivations

Freud associated later "personality types" with each of the above phases of early sexual development. He postulated that a child who remained ("fixated") at, or reverted ("regressed") to the primary phases of narcissism and polymorphous perversity would continue to exclude external reality, retain delusions of self-sufficient knowledge and power, and maintain other "perverse" behaviors into adulthood. In contrast, an adolescent or adult operating from a position of infantile orality would be passive, ineffective, and react with anger or depression to any later frustration equated with repeated weanings. Again differentially, an individual fixated in "expulsive anality" would either be socially rebellious or overcompensate by "anal retentive" traits such as obsessive moralism and compulsive meticulousness. Regrettably, Freud gave insufficient credence to the highly diverse familial and cultural influences that also greatly influence child, adolescent, and adult development.

PUBERTY AND THE "OEDIPUS COMPLEX"

Puberty, which is occurring increasingly early in well-nourished Western populations, is undoubtedly a significant event in personal development. In girls age eight to twelve, maturing ovaries eject an ovum, secrete estrogens and progesterones along with sexually stimulating hormones from the adrenal glands, and so induce menarche. In boys age nine to fourteen, testicles and their appendages descend into the scrotum and release powerful male steroids which deepen the voice, accelerate growth, escalate erotic drives, and make possible the ejaculation of active sperm for juvenile fatherhood.

Freud made these events central to a somewhat fanciful and overgeneralized metapsychology based on what he termed the "Oedipus complex." He postulated that because the pubertal boy would extend his previous maternal attachments into selecting his mother as a prime sexual object, he would wish to possess her by eliminating his father, but would then become fearful that his more powerful rival would take preventive action by depriving the young challenger of his phallus. To minimize his "castration anxiety," the contentious youth would then have the following options:

To become impotent or celibate;
To challenge his father in Casanovian promiscuity, but at the price of loveless wanderings;

To divert his libido from mother to father and generalize it into homosexuality or "sublimate" it in religious services to a heavenly Father;
Or, in social compliance, to restrain his sexuality until an extrafamilial,
monogamous relationship is sanctioned by his family and society
(Case 16).

Freud derived his term for this supposedly universal adolescent crisis
from the Greek legend of Oedipus, King of Thebes, who killed his father
and married his mother, neglecting the circumstances that Oedipus had
not known the man he had killed was his father or the woman he
married was his mother. Indeed, the legend, as immortalized in three
poetic tragedies by Sophocles, transcends the simplistic themes of patricide
and incest by epitomizing nearly every human experience from parental
rejection in infancy, survival through foster care, youthful seekings for
identity, the insubstantiality of attainments by violence or pseudo-wisdom,
the fragility of public accolades, the injustice of required atonements for
social transgressions imposed by fate, the recycling of filial conflicts, and
a final attainment of immortality. Herewith the universally significant
themes other than sexuality implicit in the classic trilogy of plays written
by the aged Sophocles four centuries before Christ:

> The Oracle of Apollo at Delphi warns Laius, King of Thebes, that his
> infant son by Queen Iocaste would slay him—as, indeed, all children
> will inevitably displace their elders. To avoid the onus of infanticide,
> Laius instead hobbles his child (as many parents otherwise do) by
> pinning his ankles together (in Greek, Oedipus means swollen feet)
> and leaves him on distant Mount Cathaeron.
>
> Oedipus is rescued by the shepherd Tiresias, who arranges to have
> the child adopted by Polybus, King of Corinth (as many rejected
> children are rescued by parent surrogates). But Oedipus is never cer-
> tain that he is really the legitimate Prince of Corinth, does not accept
> assurances from King Polybus or his Queen Merope (can anyone be
> absolutely certain of his paternity?), and is deeply troubled when he
> learns at Delphi that he is destined not only to kill his father, but also to
> marry his mother. Trying to escape his fate (as who does not?), he vows
> never to see his supposed parents Polybus or Merope again, and leaves
> Corinth to wander in search of what is now called his "personal identity."
> At a crossroads outside Thebes, an older man disputes his right of way
> and is killed in the ensuing battle (as all elders who challenge imperi-
> ous youth will be disposed of in their turn).
>
> To display his intellectual as well as physical prowess (as do modern
> youths) Oedipus also conquers a Sphinx whose "riddle" (actually the
> naive nursery puzzle about how we all start with four legs, then two,
> then three, i.e., crawl, walk and finally use a cane) he solves, and

thereby emancipates the Thebans from years of sphincteric terror. For reward, Oedipus is given the throne of Thebes vacated by King Laius whom Oedipus had unknowingly slain, and the privilege of marrying the widowed Iocaste.

But because nagging doubts remain (who does not have them?), Oedipus, after more years of renewed searching (the curse of Western man), learns from the now aged Tiresias the awful truth that he had indeed killed his father, Laius, and cohabited incestuously with his mother Iocaste—"awful" only because he fears that others would regard it so. With appropriate dramatics, he blinds (not castrates) himself in expiation (and thereby secures the advantage of being a pathetic figure), curses his own sons Eteocles and Polynices, and preempts his daughters Antigone and Ismene (as do many aging parents) to serve his declining years. Finally, at the grove of Colonus he justifies his behavior before Apollo and Athena, and himself becomes a demi-god, thus acquiring the immortal archangelic status we all believe our due.

There are, of course, many variations of these legends in Hungarian, Rumanian, Finnish, and even Lapland folklore. In another Greek version, Homer has Iocaste commit suicide, after which a more sensible Oedipus completes his reign in relative peace. But the myths are never simplistically sexual; instead, they illuminate childhood insecurities, youthful seekings, temporary triumphs, mature disillusions, and a final aspiration toward immortality.

THE FATE OF FEMINITY

As to the pubertal girl, Freud rejected Ferenczi's suggestion that her parallel conflicts be designated an "Electra complex," based on the (equally irrelevant) legend of Electra, daughter of King Agamemnon of Mycea, who wished to avenge his death by killing her faithless mother. Instead, as noted above, Freud assumed that all women (with the possible exception of his daughter Anna) would, in accord with his dictum that "anatomy determines destiny," accept their inferiority and serve men, as had his devoted mother and self-effacing wife.[8]

PSYCHOANALYTIC REFORMULATIONS

Freud's metapsychology has had wide quasi-poetic appeal, but has been repeatedly challenged for its pansexual focus, its disregard of genetic, physiologic, and cultural determinants, and its frequent lack of clinical validation. For these and other reasons many of Freud's early disciples began to differ with him by proposing motivations other than sexuality as basic to human conduct. Otto Rank held that life's greatest trauma occurred at birth, by which he meant not the breathless bodily and cerebral constrictions imposed on the fetus, but rather its experience of being ejected from a serene, all-provident uterine Nirvana into a strange, cold, glaring, inimical world, inducing what existential philosophers (Husserl, Camus, Sartre) now term the basic *angst* of existence.

Sandor Ferenczi recognized a life-long, self-protective narcissim; Adolf Adler emphasized the child's struggle for compensatory power; Margaret Mahler clarified its stresses of individuation; Ernst Kris segregated its later "conflict-free Ego"; and Karen Horney differentiated the difficulties of being "with, for, or against its social order."

Donald Winnicott, Otto Kernberg, and Heinz Kohut have reverted to Ferenczi's theme of regressive self-alienation (Case 8), modified only by the "introjection" of dehumanized interpersonal symbols as "objects" which, if inimical, engender "primal depressions," "reactive grandiosity," or a "borderline psychopathic state," all of which must be exorcised by years of individual or group "psychoanalysis of the Self" (Case 9).

Each of these concepts has some implicit value, but none has demonstrated heuristic significance in comparison to the more comprehensive and dynamic approaches to theory and therapy outlined in the chapters to follow.

ENDNOTES

1. Contrast Freud's *treiben* (sexual "drives" often mistranslated as "instincts") with Henri Bergson's postulate of a unitary *elan vitale* — a universal life force that also actuates genetic union, embryonic nutrition, growth and differentiation, followed by postnatal seekings for perceptions, cognitions, esthetics, and creativity beyond mere procreation.

2. "And the Lord God . . . breathed into Adam's nostrils the breath of life, and man became a living soul." (Genesis 2:7).

3. In Christian renunciation of sex, nuns vow to remain virginal as brides of Christ.

4. However the term "narcissistic" is hardly applicable to an infant whose immature, unmyelinated brain is incapable of such abstractions.

5. Gustatory pleasures may become paramount: Romans feasted interminably even when that necessitated repeatedly induced vomiting, whereas Americans either ignore advancing obesity or consume large servings of acaloric pablums.

6. In general, what men compose and conduct, women play and teach.

7. Many African, South Pacific, and Indonesian cultures encourage these bisexual explorations as a preparation for pubertal and adult roles.

8. Men had long preferred to blame their troubles on women: Eve was the namesake of evil and raised Cain; Babylonian Ishtar brought floods and plagues; Greek Aphrodite was the goddess of maddening aphrodisiacs; Roman Cybele was a fatal seductress. Christianity has tortured and burned a million women as witches; Islam confines them in shrouds or harems, and synagogues still segregate them in galleries safely away from contaminating the Torah. Freud himself honored Marie Bonaparte, Karen Horney, Melanie Klein, and other female disciples, especially his daughter Anna, yet some male psychoanalysts still seem to adhere to Freud's insistence on feminine inferiority.

RECOMMENDED READING

Erikson, E.H.: *Identity: Youth and Crisis.* New York, W.W. Norton, 1968.

Freud, S.: "Three contributions to the theory of sexuality," In Strachey, A. (ed.): *The Standard Edition of the Complete Psychological Works of Sigmund Freud.* London, Hogarth Press, 1953, vol. 7, pp. 125–243.

Furman, E.: *Helping Young Children Grow.* New York, International Universities Press, 1987.

Greenspan, S.I., Pollock, G.: *The Course of Life, Volume II, The Child.* New York, International Universities Press, 1988.

Kelly, G.F.: *Learning About Sex.* Woodbury, New York, Barrons Press, 1980.

Masserman, J.H.: *Psychiatry and Health.* New York, Human Sciences Press, 1986.

Money, J.: *Man and Woman, Boy and Girl.* Baltimore, Johns Hopkins Press, 1972.

Schmidt, A., Remschmedt, H. (eds.): *Child and Adolescent Psychiatry.* Lewiston, New York, Hagrefe and Huber, 1989.

Shipman, G.: The psychodynamics of sex education. *Family Coordinator, 17:*3–12, 1968.

Stoller, R.J.: *Sex and Gender.* New York, Science House, 1968.

Uribe, V.M.: Adolescents: Their special physical, social and metapsychologic needs. *Adolescence, 21:*83–96, 1986.

Chapter 3

ADOLESCENT SEXUALITY

According to recent studies, seven in ten boys and five in ten girls have had sexual intercourse by age fifteen, and about half of the 400,000 illegitimate pregnancies registered annually in the United States occur in early teenagers. Because these statistics do not include an incalculable number of unreported incidences, adolescent sexuality is manifestly a phenomenon of urgent eugenic, familial, economic, and cultural significance.

VECTORS IN ADOLESCENT SEXUALITY

Among the reasons advanced for the increase of overt sexual activity in adolescents are the following:

Familial

According to the 1986 census, 20 million American parents are not married, and even in relatively stable households, children are aware of their parents' sexual freedom (Case 16). In many homes nudity is regarded as "natural and disinhibiting" and parental intercourse may be practiced openly.

Cultural

Distinctions between popular literature and frank pornography have become tenuous; and, with decreasing restraint, films and television, in homes as well as elsewhere, exhibit nudity, portray seductions, attempted rapes and scenes of explicit coitus. Mothers take pride in dressing their teenage daughters "attractively," i.e., with special accents on hips, legs, and breasts, while fathers find surrogate virility in their sons' sexual adventures.[1]

Sexual Education

Courses in elementary and high schools (Case 7) are useful in clarifying sexual physiology, in warning youngsters about incest (Case 7), against venereal and systemic diseases, and in countering notions that nonpenetrant "fiddling," specific coital positions, or Coca-Cola douches can avert pregnancies. Such courses may also emphasize that contraceptive pills or cervical inserts require parental consent and a physician's services, and that teenage parenthood entails serious medical, social, and legal complications; however, teenagers also may learn that condoms or vaginal jellies are readily available for "safe sex,"—and many adolescents will misunderstand the instructions or disregard all cautions.

Religion

Nor are moral teachings necessarily effective; studies have shown no significant differences in sexual conduct among adolescents of variously professed faiths.[2]

Global

J. Frank and other social psychiatrists regard a recourse to sexuality as one form of escape from worldwide nuclear anxiety.

SEXUAL PRACTICES

Initiation

Teenage explorations generally begin with "petting"; kissing is usually initiated by girls as part of romantic fantasies, and only later sought and lingualized by boys. Contrectations may then progress to tactile confirmations of sexual differences, directed by boys toward budding breasts and genital folds, by girls to the phallus and testicles. Euphemized as "deep necking" such introductory maneuvers may lead only to individual or reciprocal masturbation, although genital intercourse ("scoring") may also ensue. In this regard, male teenagers distinguish "lays," reputedly available for intercourse, from "good" girls ("Marys,"

"Rebeccas") not sexually responsive but preferable on social grounds. However, such distinctions often apply only to girls in one's own racial, ethnic, economic, or religious group; others are considered fair game.

Normal male adolescents reach peak physical height and sexual drive at about age 18, after which, despite the harrowing obsessions of satyric Don Juans, virility gradually declines—although, with reasonable practice, it may be retained well into the eighties. Females are maximally developed and libidous at age 16 and can experience multiple clitoral and vaginal orgasms indefinitely.

Locale

Among economically privileged adolescents, initial sexual "passes" are most readily made in their favorite mobile hideout: the family automobile, parked after a movie or rock concert in some supposedly secluded spot. This, however, may involve bribes to scouting police (some of whom may demand libidinal privileges) and greater dangers of assaults and rapes by roving gangs. Older teenage couples can book assignments under assumed names in permissive "four-hour motels"; however, the personnel of some of these establishments have traced identities through car licenses and demanded blackmail.[3] Preferable liaisons, therefore, may be arranged in either of the couple's homes when parents are absent; indeed, if restraining adults are away for extended periods, alcohol, drugs, and group sex parties may be staged, sometimes degenerating into thoughtless vandalism and violence, with ensuing publicity and serious consequences for all concerned.

Affects

As may be inferred, sheer inconvenience, guilt, mistrust, and dread of disease or pregnancy vitiate initial sexual anticipations and often result in erectile impotence confronted with vaginal spasms; ergo, less than half of teenage boys and only one in five girls report that their first attempts at genital intercourse were satisfactory. Nevertheless, because solitary masturbation does not long satisfy male aspirations to assertive virility or feminine longings for desirability, heterosexual explorations soon recur, often entailing new frustrations, jealousies, reactive promiscuity, and other vicissitudes as outlined below.[4]

SPECIFIC SEXUAL DYSFUNCTIONS

Phallic

Teenagers may have erections during restless REM (rapid eye movement) sleep, but become impotent when attempting intercourse under physically unpleasant or anxiety-provoking circumstances (Cases 3 and 4). If initially potent, about one in five adolescents experiences premature or dry ejaculation during coitus, again attributable either to sexual inhibitions or excessive use of drugs (alcohol, amphetamines, cocaine), or to some physical disorder such as undiagnosed diabetes.

Vaginal

Teenage girls with maintained inhibitions (Case 5), and especially after inappropriate foreplay, may lack vaginal lubrication and experience painful intercourse, with discomfort increased by local inflammations, or the pressure of a displaced uterus.

SOCIAL COMPLICATIONS

Drugs

Teenage abuses of alcohol, sedatives, stimulants, and, most seriously cocaine and opiate derivatives (Chapter 9), with consequent impairments of social inhibitions may induce individual or gang rapes.

Prostitution

All of the teenage sexual vicissitudes outlined above, if further complicated by parental neglect or abuse, poverty, or the insistent demands of a drug addiction, may lead to the added tragedies of adolescent prostitution, with its attendant diseases, criminal entanglements, and accelerated personal and social deterioration.

SEXUALLY-TRANSMITTED DISEASES

Gonorrheal infections, frequent in adolescents, may spread to testicles, Fallopian tubes, and ovaries. Herpes viruses cause recurrent genital and anal blisters, and the papillomatous varieties may precede cervical cancers. Untreated syphilis may cause irreversible damage to the brain and spinal cord. Venereal diseases may also either prevent pregnancy or irretrievably injure the fetus.

AIDS

AIDS, caused by the human immunodeficiency virus (HIV) transmitted through sexual contacts or infected needles, has become a leading cause of early death among teenage drug users, particularly blacks and Hispanics.

Prevention comprises sexual abstinence or reliable condoms, avoidance of mucous extragenital contacts (e.g., lingual kissing) and the use of carefully sterilized needles.[5] At this writing there is no cure for AIDS; however, many so infected may live for many years on balanced nutrition, low-dose vitamins, and symptomatic medications. This regime, when supplemented by individual or group therapy and religious counselling, facilitates morale-building, occupational, esthetic, and recreational activities.

The medical and psychologic treatment of the above complications of teenage sexuality will be more comprehensively discussed in special chapters to follow.

ENDNOTES

1. In a Latin-Iberian tradition the father may habitually spend his mid-day *siesta* with a mistress, and both father and son may receive sexual favors from household maids.

2. Judeo-Christian-Islamic archives apparently condone devious sexuality. In the Old Testament (Genesis 11), Abraham (neé Abram of Ur) offered to prostitute his wife Sarai to ensure his own safety in Egypt; later, he impregnated Sarai's maid Hagar and "cast her out" along with his child. Abraham's other son, Isaac, likewise indentured his wife Rebbecca to King Abumelech of the Philistines. Lot, for the sake of hospitality offered his two virgin daughters to a group of Sodomites. At Yaweh's behest, Joshua's warriors killed all the Medianite men and wives and enslaved the remaining virgins. King David sent his lieutenant Uriah to a military death in order to pre-empt his widow, Bathsheba, into the royal harem.

There are troublesome examples also in the New Testament: Mary Magdalen's harlotry is later glorified. Jesus justified violence in the Holy Temple and proclaimed: "I bring you not peace but a sword." His disciples ignored their familial responsibilities and also deserted Him when their own safety was threatened.

Nor, as commanded in the Koran, have all converts to Islam been "merciful in the name of Allah." In the Middle Ages, Islam preserved Greek civilization, yet Muslim princes slaughtered infidels, drowned harem inmates considered no longer desirable, and abandoned multiple wives with the simple formula "I divorce thee."

3. Many concerned parents are therefore beginning to wonder whether it would be preferable to follow the Scandanavian practice of acknowledging and providing safe opportunities for teenage sexuality, which, instead of being derided as "puppy love," may be sincere and chacterologically productive.

4. Many states require parental consent for the abortion of a minor and, according to a 1973 Supreme Court decision, now sub durice, all abortions after twelve weeks of pregnancy involve complicated medical and legal procedures.

5. AIDS may also be transmitted through infected blood transfusions and from mother to child. The U.S. Public Health Service reported in 1988 that 1.5 million Americans had been infected with HIV, each with a life expectancy of 18 to 36 months. Concurrently, the World Health Organization estimated that five million people world-wide had also been infected, with a million new cases likely within the next five years.

RECOMMENDED READING

Erman, A.H. (Ed.): *The Psychology of Adolescence.* New York, International Universities Press, 1973.

Goodman, J.M. (Ed.): *Sexual Abuse.* Chicago, Year Book, 1989.

Jensen, G.D.: Cross-cultural studies of sex. In Sadock, B.J., Kaplan, H.I. and Freedman, A.M.: *The Sexual Experience.* New York, Williams and Wilkins, 1976.

Money, J., Erhardt, K.: *Man and Woman, Boy and Girl.* Baltimore, Johns Hopkins University Press, 1972.

Sorenson, R.E. *Adolescent Sexuality.* New York: World Press, 1973.

Uribe, V.M. Adolescents: Their special physical, social and metapsychologic needs. *Adolescence 21:*83–96, 1986.

Chapter 4

ATTENDANT BEHAVIORAL DISORDERS

Deviations of conduct in adolescence can be attributed to anticipated or actual frustrations of three ultimate and urgent (Ur) needs of sentient human beings at all ages. Briefly formulated, these needs are:

Ur 1, Physical: For the vitality and skills necessary to maintain environmental control
Ur 2, Social: For the alliances essential to interpersonal securities
Ur 3, Existential: For the beliefs and faiths requisite to serenity

RANGE OF ADAPTATIONS

Normally, the child through adolescence who is adequately fed, clothed, and taught basic self-care, feels relatively safe in his family, and extends this security into anticipating a reasonably beneficent universe. Under various physical, familial, and sociocultural handicaps the adolescent may still adapt constructively as follows:

Ur I

By developing special talents to compensate for physical handicaps. Homer, born blind, wrote the Iliad and Odyssey; stuttering Demosthenes became an impelling orator; epileptic Caesar glorified Rome. Itzhak Perlman, crippled since childhood, is a supreme violin virtuoso; Stephen Hawkins, a paraplegic, is the world's leading cosmophysicist.

Few disadvantaged adolescents will reach such heights; but many will approach them to the world's benefit.

Ur II

If deprived of familial securities, adolescents may find them in surrogate teachers or coaches, in peer friendships, and in social organizations monitored by concerned and empathetic adults devoted to youth welfare.[1]

Ur III

Since no one can ever be absolutely certain of either health or mortal friends, an unquestioning faith in an invocable and protective providence is a third basic human need.[2] Fortunately, religious movements among current youth, if not fanatic, can provide desirable guidance and some measure of existential serenity.

All of these adaptive maneuvers can include "normal" childhood and adolescent sexual expressions; i.e., those culturally acceptable with regard to age, time, and place.

RANGE OF MALADAPTATIONS

Conversely, childhood sexuality may take the following deviant forms again marshalled under the basic Ur-parameters:

Ur I, Physical

Male adolescents, often overstimulated by injections of adrenal or testicular hormones, may strive for excessive muscular strength and sexual virility, endangering their health and longevity while neglecting their education and the development of cognitive and social skills. Girls may also overemphasize physical attractiveness while disregarding their more promising intellectual and esthetic potentialities.

Ur II, Social

Protests against parental or other discipline may range from verbal defiances of authority, through furtively placed graffiti on schools and public buildings, to violence against teachers and police. Deprived of what they consider is due them, adolescents may steal from siblings and parents, proceed to neighborhood burglaries or, in desperation, to armed robberies of peers and adults.

Vagabondage

Adolescents' attempts to escape from what they eventually regard as an unbearable environment may range from school dropouts through recurrent vagrancies[3] to a permanent nomadism in search of distant utopias, usually with ill-starred results.

Group Delinquencies

Seeking friendships and supposed protection for individual transgressions, alienated adolescents may join, or be recruited into regional gangs, conceived as quasi "families" with pseudo-parental "godfathers" and peer siblings (i.e., the fancied Cosa Nostra). They can then be induced to participate in criminal activities such as conjoint robberies, assaults, gang rapes, and an ultimate form of savagery termed "wilding."

Ur III, Existential

With distorted self images, adolescents become addicted to alcohol, barbiturates ("downers"), amphetamines ("uppers"), marijuana ("pot"), opiates, or even various forms of cocaine ("crack") to achieve temporary insensitivities to pain, tension, and sorrow, or hallucinatory exhilaration that outweigh the ensuing physical agonies.

All of the above aberrations may be accompanied by deviant sexual activities as described in Chapter 3. Obviously poverty, familial disorganization, deficiencies in our educational system, ethnic, racial and religious prejudices, social and legal injustices, and other grave stresses on our youth induce and enhance their transgressions, and should, therefore, enlist therapists in social and political reforms beyond the scope of this chapter.

ENDNOTES

1. Classical Sparta separated its youth from their homes for early, extensive and continuous military training; partly because its soldiers had few familial loyalties, Sparta was eventually defeated. Children in Israeli kibbutsim also live in separate dormitories during their education, but visit their working parents every evening to maintain familial and cultural allegiances, and have therefore later valiantly defended their homeland.

2. This was perverted: In the 13th Century when 100,000 children, misled by the mad St. Stephen, joined a Crusade to liberate the Holy Land from the Turks, only to be enslaved enroute or to perish from hunger and disease.

3. The city of Denver pays vagrant girls a dollar a day for avoiding impregnation; however, it is doubtful that such inducements would materially affect the national incidence of teenage pregnancy.

RECOMMENDED READING

Esman, A.H. (Ed.): *The Psychology of Adolescence.* New York, International Universities Press, 1973.

Masserman, J.H.: *Psychiatry and Health.* New York, Human Sciences Press, 1987.

Masserman, J.H. (Ed.): *Youth, a Transcultural Approach.* New York, Grune and Stratton, 1969.

Sadock, B.J., Kaplan, H.I. and Freedman, A.M.: *The Sexual Experience.* Baltimore, Williams and Wilkins, 1976.

Uribe, V.M.: Adolescents: Their special physical, social and metapsychologic needs. *Adolescence, 21:*83–96, 1986.

Chapter 5

DIAGNOSIS OF ADOLESCENT DISORDERS

Auguste Comte (1798–1857), an astute French scientist, traced the development of human thought through three phases:

Mystical. All events were believed to be controlled by supernatural spirits or deities who, fortunately, could be beseeched, cajoled, or bribed to redirect events in Man's favor. Such faiths persist in modern religions to mitigate mankind's physical and social insecurities.[1]

Classificatory. In a succeeding phase, unknown causation became subsidiary to notions that all phenomena could be marshaled into currently convenient categories. Early Greek philosophers considered all things to be mixtures of earth, air, water, and fire, and a century ago the Mendelejef Periodic Table still listed precisely 87 immutable chemical elements.[2] Carl Jung classified all human beings as being either "introvert" or "extrovert," whereas William James separated them into the "tender or tough minded," leading Bertrand Russell to remark wryly that if there really were only two "types" of human beings, one "type" must believe that there can be such simple classifications.

Dynamic. In this third phase all phenomena—a term implying the observer's input—are recognized as infinitely variable resultants of a multiplicity of influences, only some of which we can now (or perhaps ever) determine or control.[3]

RELEVANCE TO ADOLESCENT BEHAVIOR

Correspondingly, teenage conduct, as indicated in Chapter 4, manifests a complex interplay of genetic, somatic, familial, environmental, intellectual, educational, and sociocultural influences, and probably others yet to be analyzed. As a consequence, no two adolescents are alike, and no designation can adequately categorize the admixture of dependencies, anxieties, obsessions, compulsions, aggressions, depressions, regressions, and maladaptive patterns developed at various times and in variable degree by every teenager. Nevertheless, because insurance, industrial, legal, and governmental agencies require that a therapist, for "research" or "statistical purposes," label an adolescent patient with a term listed in an official Diagnostic and Statistical Manual (usually the American Psychiatric Association DSM III–R), some nosologic epithet must be furnished, preferably with full recognition of its descriptive, therapeutic, or prognostic inadequacies and even more importantly, that it does not prejudice the treatment and welfare of the adolescent. Examples of such semantically and clinically misleading appellations are the following:

Hysteria, currently meaning nonorganic sensory or muscular dysfunctions (Case 1), dates from Plato's notion that disturbed women (and effeminate men) suffered from an internally wandering uterus (Greek *hysterus*),[4] Malingering stems from Latin *malignitas,* evil, and J. Frank's term "demoralization" similarly retains medieval concepts of ethical transgressions. Neurosis, a word coined by William Cullen in the 18th century to indicate inflammations of the nerves, is now applied to variable inhibitions (Case 5), obsessions, phobias, compulsions (Case 12), and other idiosyncracies (e.g., sexual promiscuity) not quite in accord with "normal" cultural patterns, shading into borderline or sociopathic syndromes which imply socially disruptive behavior (Case 13). Even more pejoratively the designation of "psychosis" (Greek, disorded *psyche,* soul) connotes fixations of mood such as in *melancholia* (Case 6) or mania (Latin, *frenzy*), whereas "schizophrenia" (Latin, split mind) is applied to "dereistic" (Cases 10, 11) sensory misinterpretations (illusions, hallucinations) or locally unacceptable beliefs (delusions), suspicions and actions (paranoia). Legally, however, only when the attendant dis-orders of conduct become personally or socially dangerous can official sanctions be obtained for the imposed administration of psychoactive drugs or protective institutionalization (Case 15).

Manifestly, none of the above "clinical diagnoses" adequately indicates the nature or intensity of the cognitive, affective, or behavioral aberrations they purport to describe, their genetic or experiential causes, their admixtures of symptoms, their prognosis, the therapies required, or other essential connotations; instead, the semantic and heuristic deficiencies of our current terminology may be illustrated by the following:

In our precarious times, when does anxiety over imminent atomic genocide become "phobic," or persistent concern about the proliferation of nuclear weapons become "obsessive"? At what stage does meticulous cleanliness in the operating room (or kitchen) become "compulsive"? Is a choice of premarital or sexual chastity necessarily a "neurotic inhibition"? What reclusive, rebellious, or otherwise highly idiosyncratic authors or artists throughout history (e.g., Nietszche, Paganini) would now be termed "borderline personalities"? By what current criteria can a stridently vocal or actively militant protester against what he or she terms racial discrimination or economic injustice be judged a "paranoiac" who is "disturbing the peace"? Whose peace? At what point does religious faith and devotion become illusional? When, a century and a half ago, Marie Bernarde Soubrous, an ailing adolescent communed repeatedly with the Virgin Mary at a spring in Lourdes, France, was she "psychotic," or "divinely inspired," as proclaimed by Pope Pius XI? Was he then himself delusional in immortalizing her as the saintly founder of the Shrine of Bernadette where the blessed waters and commemorative rituals have reputedly healed thousands of sufferers? What subcommittee of which psychiatric society shall set these sweeping distinctions?

We may further personalize the issue as follows:

We have all spent our lifetimes in obsessive-compulsive conformity to cultural rituals, failing which, we have all felt anxieties, sometimes approaching panic with severe somatic dysfunctions. We have all been pressed down (de-pressed) by excessive environmental stresses, and have reacted with destructive impulses toward ourselves and others, or sought surcease in dereistic, "schizoid" beliefs and behavior. And we shall all inevitably resent the physical and intellectual obsolescence of advancing age. The essence of empathy is "There, but for the grace of providence go I."

CLINICAL DIAGNOSIS

Therapists, then, differ from their patients or clients only in the intensities, durations, expressions, and influencability of "normal" or culturally deviant patterns of thought and conduct—a parallelism constituting an invaluable source of communication and empathy. Corresponding aberrations from socially acceptable behavior in adolescence, or at any age, cannot be meaningfully relegated to any simplistic classification; instead, a clinical diagnosis (Greek *dia-gnoskeien*, thorough understanding) must include a comprehensive survey of the interplay of (1) the remote and recent genetic, physiologic, experiential and social stresses that occasioned the teenager's past and current maladaptations, (2) an appraisal of the nature, severity, variability[5], and reversability of the current symptoms, (3) his or her physical resilience, salutory motivations, intelligence, special talents, and other characterologic resources, and (4) the prospects for their utilization through (5) varied combinations of medical, environmental, and psychologic modes of therapy designed (6) to restore optimal personal and social adaptations. If some arithmetic appellation is still required for computer storage, the authors' nonpejorative favorite, applicable in most instances (typical exceptions, Cases 11 and 13) is Adjustment Disorder, DSM III–R (329) with Dysthymia (230). Indeed, the authors freely admit that during their adolescence (and thereafter) they, too, may have adapted suboptimally to life's stresses, with intercurrent behavioral and emotional manifestations with which the readers of this volume, may retrospectively empathize.

ENDNOTES

1. Comte, himself in need of mystic companionship and strength in his later years, founded a cult in which he and his acolytes worshipped his deceased wife Clothilde, as the beneficent Queen of Heaven who would grant them immortality.

2. Compare with current concepts of an as yet irreducible number of variably evanescent subatomic wave-particles.

3. Leo Kanner, a founder of child psychiatry, cautioned one of us (JHM) when a student at Johns Hopkins that "understanding quantum mechanics is child's play compared to understanding child's play."

4. Another Greek notion was that epilepsy (literally, stroke from above) was a punishment from the gods.

5. As but one example, most psychedelic drugs diminish libido, but compensate by relieving sexual inhibitions; ergo, depending on his drug intake, a late adolescent may be impotent one day and a satyr the next. However, addicts of both sexes may prefer their drug "highs" to erotic fulfillments.

RECOMMENDED READING

American Psychiatric Association: *Diagnostic and Statistical Manual of Mental Disorders,* 3rd Edition-Revised, Washington, D.C., 1987.

Braceland, F.J.: Classification, past, present and future. *Psychiatric Annals, 6:*349–367, 1976.

Klerman, G.I., Vaillant, G.E., Michels, R., et al.: A debate on DSM III. *Am. J. Psychiat. 141:*539–558, 1984.

Masserman, J.H.: *A Psychiatric Odyssey.* New York, Science House, 1971.

Masserman, J.H.: *Theory and Therapy in Dynamic Psychiatry.* New York, Aronson, 1973.

Sartorius, N.: Diagnosis and classification. *Mental Health and Society. 5:*79–85, 1978.

Uribe, V.M.: Transtornos de la personalidad en la Adolescencia. In *Medicina del Adolescente,* Bogota, Colombia, S.A., Ediciones Rosaristas, 1981.

Van Harselt, V.B. and Hersen, M.: *Handbook of Adolescent Psychology.* Elmsford, New York, Pergamon Press, 1987.

Chapter 6

PRINCIPLES OF THERAPY

As president of the American Psychiatric Association, one of us (JHM) organized and, over a period of five years, participated in an intensive interdisciplinary study of more than 120 modes of treating human behavior disorders at various ages. An analysis of the voluminous data so acquired indicated essentially (a) that patients seek help when their vital strengths and skills, interpersonal securities, and/or existential faiths seem threatened (Chapter 4) and (b) that to be effective, any treatment had to mitigate these triune urgent (Ur) anxieties by utilizing the following therapeutic modalities[1]:

1. *The reputation* of the therapist as a professionally competent and erudite mentor.

2. *The establishment of rapport* leading to mutual trust and confidence.

3. *An anamnestic[2] review* to clarify both the recent precipitating, and previous experiential causes of the patient's difficulties.

4. *The concurrent initial relief* of symptoms through all available medical means and the alleviation of environmental, psychologic, and social stresses.

5. *The reeducation* of the patient to recognize that, even at the price of foregoing dependent, preemptive, vengeful, escapist, or other dereistic gratifications, more rationally adaptive and creative patterns of conduct would be to his or her ultimate advantage.

6. *Rehabilitation* to guide the patient in applying merely cognitive verbal "insights" to realistic improvements in mutually satisfactory familial, sexual, occupational, and esthetic relationships.

7. *The progressive recapitulation* of the above throughout the course of therapy until reasonably successful physical, social, and cultural readaptations have been achieved.

These dynamic vectors may be specifically applied in the treatment of the behavioral and attendant sexual disorders of adolescents as follows:

Reputation

The parents or others concerned with the teenager may have selected the therapist on the basis of his or her ethnicity, religion, academic status, publications or social position; however, these and other qualifications may weigh far less with the prospective patient than the therapist's standing among the youth of the community as being sympathetic to juvenile needs and helpful in resolving adolescent problems. The therapist can, of course, cultivate both sources of confidence.

Rapport

The therapist should modify routine receptionist rituals by personally greeting the adolescent and ushering him or her directly into a quiet, comfortable office not overburdened with forbidding files and authoritative certificates. Following tactful references to the reasons for the interview, the therapist may identify his own projected roles: as a physician able, to relieve somatic dysfunction, as a confidante to share the adolescent's concerns, and as an experienced counselor and guide to help resolve familial, school, sexual, social, or legal difficulties. In no respect will the therapist function as a priest, policeman, judge, or other disciplinarian except when, again as a genuine friend, it might become necessary to prevent or modify some impulsive action that would seriously imperil the adolescent's welfare. Throughout these communications, best interspersed with invited comments from the adolescent, the therapist speaks simply and sincerely, avoiding any aspects of condescension or artificiality such as adopting current juvenile jargon.

However, despite such reassurances, the adolescent's initial feelings toward the therapist may continue to reflect those he or she had previously developed toward other significant persons in his or her life. These attitudes (technically termed "transference") may therefore range from subversive dependence and control ("Then help me get [dad, the school principal, the truant officer, et al.] off my back") through self-protective distancing ("Thanks for the advice; now I can take care of things and don't need to come again,") or suspicion and mistrust, ("Everyone sooner or later gets down on me,") to frank hostility ("You [and my family, school, police, et al.] just want to put me away, and if you try that, I know what to do"). Such statements may evoke the therapist's "countertransference," ranging correspondingly from the quasi-parental ("This youngster is. like my own troubled, appealing, grateful, talented son [or daughter, niece, nephew] who needs sympathy, care, and help") through the abstractly clinical ("An interesting case for the book I'm writing") to defensive wariness or covert antagonism ("He [or she] reminds me of a previous [delinquent, aggressive, vagrant, suicidal or schizoid] teenager who caused me much trouble [notoriety, legal involvements, etc.]"). Obviously, these reciprocal psychologic sets, if not recognized and resolved as indicated below, are deterrents to effective rapport and treatment.

Requisite likewise is the initial resolution of familial conflicts that affect the adolescent. This can be expedited in joint interviews at which those concerned clarify their interpersonal difficulties, and receive added assurances that their individual interests will be respected and served. With the understanding that confidentiality will be preserved, each participant may also be individually interviewed and encouraged to express what he or she had previously withheld, and then enrolled in family-oriented treatment. The adolescent is then given a series of appointments with the understanding that no one else will again be involved except as requested, or as required in special emergencies.

Review

The anamnesis should initially concentrate on the adolescent's immediate concerns: somatic dysfunctions, familial turmoils, troubled peer relationships, sexual difficulties, and social and legal complications ranging from school absenteeism through vandalism, vagrancy, drug addiction and petty crimes to major ones such as auto theft, firesetting (Case 13), robbery, rape, and violence. The therapist may already have received information from other sources about the reasons for the referral, and can compare this information (without necessarily revealing its nature or origin) with relevant comments from the patient. As further rapport is won, the adolescent will increasingly comply with tactful invitations to confide ever more freely his or her experiences, values, objectives, hopes, fantasies, attainments, and disappointments. Sexual dysfunctions and anxieties (seductions, jealousies, perversions, promiscuities, pregnancies, abortions) can then be discussed with empathy and objectivity.[3]

Forensic

If the adolescent had been referred for counselling while on court parole (usually for stealing, drug trafficking, sex offenses, or violence) an appropriately worded communication to the parole officer or other official to the effect that, although the therapist cannot take responsibility for further transgressions and must comply with the court order to report them, optimum efforts will be made to improve the youngster's behavior—a statement shared with the adolescent that often strengthens his or her need for therapy (Cases 7 and 14).

Relief

Environmental

Appropriate initial actions may be taken to ease the adolescent's pressing school, work or legal difficulties by tactful telephone calls or letters, preferably written in his or her presence for added reassurance.

Physical

If indicated, and with parents' authorization, a preliminary physical/neurological examination may be performed to check the adolescent's complaints of headache, vertigo, fatigue, or other somatic symptoms. Supplementary laboratory studies may, for example, disclose an unsuspected diabetes or hypothyroidism (Case 2) which, if treated with parental cooperation, will remove many symptoms (itching, urinary frequency, fatigue, dietary peculiarities, etc.) that may have previously been considered "neurotic." Electroencephalography may indicate the cerebral origin of tics, word repetitions, muscle spasms, and seizures, or episodes of blankness or unaccountable rages. Genetic studies may indicate an XO strain in girls (slothfulness, physical, sexual, and intellectual retardation) which may be countered by the balanced administration of ovarian hormones; so also, in XXY in boys (impulsiveness, pseudo-virilism, and hypersexuality) may partially respond to testosterone inhibitors.

Sedation

If there are no contraindications, medications for restlessness, anorexia, insomnia, or other manifestations of anxiety or depression may, at appropriate times, be prescribed, but with due caution that the adolescent not add the sedatives or antidepressants to his covert intake of other drugs and increase the abuse of both.

However, telltale marks of subdural or intravenous drug injections, especially of crack or heroin, may call for a family conclave as to the advisability of isolation from the drug supply and hospitalization for monitored withdrawal and training in abstention.

Venereal diseases must be reported in most states to the local department of health, but may be confidentially treated either by the therapist or by referral to a urogenital specialist. Finally, a positive AIDS test, mandatorily reportable, poses devastating personal, familial, and public concerns, mitigated only by reassurances of asexual nontransmittability, alleviation by AZT and other medication, maintenance of general health, and hopes for the early discovery of a cure.

Reeducation

Successive interviews (literally, exchange of views) varying in frequency, from two or more weekly to monthly, and in length from 30 to 90 minutes or more as required, examine the adolescent's past and present relationships with parents, siblings and peers, incidental frustrations, disappointments, anxieties, hostilities and escapisms, and their extensions to extrafamilial dealings with teachers, ministers, police and other surrogates, implicitly or explicitly including the therapist. The adolescent's resultant familial, scholastic, sexual, and social maladaptations are concurrently clarified, and alternative responses explored as possibly preferable, not on the basis of arbitrarily prescribed parental, cultural, or even legal edicts, but primarily for the adolescent's own current and future advantage.

Sexuality

Here, caution must be exercised in instructing the adolescent as to sexual techniques, the prevention of venereal disease or modes of contraception; because, as more specifically discussed in Chapter 7, such advice may be misapplied by the adolescent, alienate his or her family, terminate the therapy, and possibly subject the therapist to legal sanctions.

At various junctures, preferably with the adolescent's consent, a family conference may be called to review progress and to agree on joint actions for the best interests of all concerned (Case 1).

Rehabilitation

This subparameter comprises reliable indications of desirable changes in behavior, supplemented by objective reports from the patient's family, teachers, employers, or, in court cases, parole officers, that the adolescent is indeed applying the intellectual and affective insights acquired as above to significant improvements in his/her familial, educational, sexual, and social conduct.

Recapitulation

Progress in treatment is often jagged: rapport is challenged, communications falter, insights require further clarification, and long-standing behavioral patterns recur and resist change. Nevertheless, improvement generally occurs, and when reasonably adequate for the adolescent's physical well-being and social comity and creativity, therapy can be suspended with only occasional follow-up interviews, or renewal should circumstances again warrant.

In essence, this chapter has outlined the general principles of therapy with adolescents. Special techniques applicable to specific behavioral problems are discussed in the following chapters and exemplified in case citations.

ENDNOTES

1. For ready recall, all the vectors of treatment are termed to begin alliteratively with the letter "*r.*"

2. A personal anamesis differs dynamically from a mere recounting of life events in that their significance for the patient is investigated and clarified.

3. Contrary to many current concepts, transient and somatically noninjurious, parent-child or intersibling sexual relations, even when verified, usually leave no serious adverse effects, and require only judicious avoidance of social and legal traumata. However, accounts of incest pose special problems for the therapist, in that laws in many states require that sexual abuse by parents or close family members

must be reported to the police. The therapist is then faced with a dilemma (Chapter 8): either obey the law and subject the offending adult to justifiable legal action (Case 14), or, at considerable personal risk, preserve confidentiality and resort to family counselling as a preferable solution (Case 7). Nevertheless, if incest is due to, or induces, psychiatric disorders in the participants, and is accompanied by familial disruptions, violence, and/or consanguinous pregnancy, combinations of the modes of therapy described in this chapter become necessary.

RECOMMENDED READING

A.P.A. Commission on Therapies: *The Psychiatric Therapies.* Washington, D.C., American Psychiatric Association, 1985.

Czikzentmihaly, M. and Larson, R.: *Adolescent Therapy.* New York, Basic Books, 1984.

Fishman, E.C.: *Treating Troubled Adolescents.* New York, Basic Books, 1984.

Giovacchini, P.: Psychiatric treatment of the adolescent. In Kaplan, H.I., Freedman, A.M. and Sadock, B.J. (Eds.): *Comprehensive Textbook of Psychiatry.* Baltimore, Williams and Wilkins, 1980, pp. 2706–2716.

Masserman, J.H.: *Handbook of Psychiatric Therapies.* New York, Science House, 1966.

Sadock, B.J., Kaplan, H.I., Freedman, A.M.: *The Sexual Experience.* Baltimore, Williams and Wilkins, 1976.

Salzman, L., Masserman, J.H.: *Modern Concepts of Psychoanalysis.* New York, Philosophical Library, 1962.

Uribe, V.M.: Short-term psychotherapy of adolescents. *J. Amer. Acad. Psychoan., 16:*27–31, 1988.

Wolberg, L.: *Techniques of Psychotherapy.* New York, Grune and Stratton, 1978.

Chapter 7

SEXUAL COUNSELLING

COUNSELLING ADOLESCENTS

On the basis of vague complaints to parents and others about being "nervous" or "just unhappy," teenagers may be referred for therapy when all they really want is confidential resolution of their sexual concerns: apart from general awkwardness and bewilderment, the boy may be troubled about his partial or complete impotence; the girl about her fear and frigidity. As indicated in previous chapters, such difficulties, when not due to anatomic impediments, can usually be traced to familial or cultural trepidations and guilts, the alleviation of which would release mutually satisfactory libidinal relationships. If, however, the adolescent insists on the necessity for elaborate guidance in erotic techniques, the therapist is presented with the following dilemmas:

1. If he or she declines on the grounds that such explicit instruction would be misleading and ineffective, the adolescent may seek "sex therapy" elsewhere.

2. If the therapist furnishes the sexual tutoring he or she runs these risks:

(a) The adolescent will extend his or her erotic explorations, often with renewed failures, feelings of inadequacy and antitherapeutic resentments.

(b) The parents will observe the teenager's retained anxieties and depressions, and join in criticizing the therapy.

(c) In the unhappy event that the sexual advice "succeeds," a teenage paternity or pregnancy may subject the therapist to a suit for malpractice, and in some states, to a charge of criminally contributing to the delinquency of a minor.

The following options may, therefore, be adopted:

1. The boy is advised to obtain the desired information from his father, or the girl from her mother, despite various typical objections, such as:

41

(a) "I'd be quizzed crazy about what trouble I'd gotten into," or

(b) "I would just be told I was too young even to think about such things," or

(c) "If I went only to dad [or mom] the other would start a family fight," or

(d) "They'd send me to our minister [rabbi or priest] for a lecture on morals [and anyway,]"

(e) "*You're* supposed to be the expert they sent me to."

These evasions may sometimes be countered by assurrances that, with tact and circumspection, seeking parental guidance may actually alleviate familial mistrusts that contributed to the adolescent's difficulties in the first place. However, if this maneuver is not effective in the early phase of therapy, other courses remain:

2. The therapist ostensibly accepts the adolescent's demands for explicit instructions, but emphasizes the following preliminary cautions:

(a) The first sexual experience is always a deeply meaningful and sometimes highly disturbing event, especially for young girls.

(b) Contrary to teenage macho myths, a "no!" does not always mean a bashfully hidden "yes!"

(c) Undue persuasions, humiliations, threats, or seductive manipulations may lead to accusations of rape, with serious familial, social, and legal consequences for all concerned.

(d) Even when there is ready assent,[1] the wise adolescent had best be certain that the prospective partner's covert purposes are not to punish another lover, or to obligate and possess the present one, or to induce pregnancy for dependency reasons, or to vent covert hostility by transmitting a venereal disease, or for a variety of other reasons inimical to the adolescent's interests.

The latter consideration can also lead to sincere warnings as to the physical dangers of unguarded sex (Chapter 6): gonorrhea (signalled by genital discharges, urinary pain and pudendal distress), viral infections (recurrently disfiguring vesicles), syphilis (delayed ulcers and debilitating systemic disease), and the increasing frequency of AIDS, initially undetected but ultimately fatal.

Some adolescents will disregard these (and all other) cautions as merely outmoded preachments, some will accept them in good faith, and still others will proceed with pleas such as "But if everything is all right, and we really like [or "love"] each other, and I don't want to hurt her [or his] feelings, I still need sex advice I can't get elsewhere."[2]

3. Here again, various options are available in differing combinations, among them:

(a) The adolescent can be advised, again in all sincerity, that whatever "procedures" he or she may eventually employ, "love-making" cannot be mutually satisfactory if conceived and conducted as crudely and mechanically as the term "screwing" implies; instead, sexuality should be a truly friendly relationship in which each partner is sensitive to and considerate of the other's desires and expectations.

(b) If this aphorism is tentatively accepted, but still considered insufficiently instructive as to operational details, the adolescent may be referred to the prodigal literature on erotic techniques, with the following qualifications:

(1) Most of the "how to" paperback booklets that fill secretive "adult only" bookshops (and increasingly large sections of commercial bookstores) are, in essence, pornographic rather than helpfully informative, and may be seriously misleading.

(2) Professional texts (such as Donald Holmes' on illustrated coital positions, Helen Kaplan's on orgasmic attainments, Kaplan, Freeman and Sadock on venereal precautions, or Masters and Johnson on modes of sex therapy) are technically reliable, but may be difficult to apply without expert physical guidance to both partners.

(3) In any case, the therapist will be available to clarify whatever information the adolescent gathers from any source in the context of the prime principles of satisfactory sexual relationships: sensitivity, caution, and interpersonal care.

COUNSELLING PARENTS

In essence, parents who have read and considered this chapter with perceptive intelligence and empathy, will need little instruction as to the joint counselling of troubled adolescents. However, not all parents have the requisite qualifications (Case 10).

ENDNOTES

1. As male teenagers become aging Lotharios, they may find a challenging "yes!" no longer quite welcome.

2. Reminiscent of an analytic patient who dreamed she had been kidnapped and had inquired of her abductor: "What are you going to do to me?"—to which he replied, "How should I know; it's your dream."

RECOMMENDED READING

Calderone, M.S. (Ed): *Manual of Contraceptive Practice.* Baltimore, Williams and Wilkins, 1964, pp 104–119.

Hegeler, I., Hegeler, S.: *An ABZ of Love.* New York, Medical Press, 1963.

Holmes, D.J.: *Psychotherapy.* (Introduction by J.H. Masserman). New York, Little, Brown, 1972, pp 620–664.

Kaplan, H.: *The Illustrated Manual of Sex Therapy.* New York, Quadrangle/The New York Times Book Company, 1975.

Masters, W., Johnson, V.: *Human Sexual Inadequacy.* Boston, Little, Brown, 1970.

Sadock, B.J., Kaplan, H.I., Freedman, A.M.: *The Sexual Experience.* Baltimore, Williams and Wilkins, 1976.

Chapter 8

INCEST

Definition

Incest is defined legally as sexual intercourse between parents and their offspring or between other closely consanguinous individuals, and constitutes a criminal act in many jurisdictions in the United States and abroad.

History

Contrary to a Freudian supposition that incest was prohibited by a primal human taboo, it was indigenous in primitive tribes. Historically, it was not proscribed in the Code of Hammurabi (18th century BC) and was practiced by the Babylonian and Egyptian nobility to preserve their divine lineage. However, because incest often elicited familial jealousies and conflicts, priests and jurists evolved edicts against consanguinous sexuality until it was condemned as fatally sinful and felonious, in Judaic[1] and then in Christian and Islamic cultures.

Incidence

About fifty thousand cases of incest involving adolescents, usually among the poor and socially deprived, are recorded annually in the U.S., most frequently between father and daughter, rarely between mother (usually widowed) and young son. This statistic manifestly does not include unreported instances, especially among siblings at all social levels, or in secret rites in isolated communities.

PSYCHODYNAMICS

Many circumstances contributory to incest have been proposed, among them:

Sexual mistreatment of the offending parent during his or her childhood;

Frigidity on the part of the wife, who may overtly or covertly wish to control her husband by substituting his daughter;

Poverty which necessitates crowded living quarters and limits external relationships;

Seductions on the part of teenagers who wish to gain familial privileges;

Esoteric ethnic or cultist rituals, often vigorously defended by the family;

Misuse of alcohol or drugs that further disinhibit sexual interactions;

Social and legal tolerance for incestuous behavior.

Various combinations of these vectors require the comprehensive clinical appraisals and integrated therapies outlined below.

VERIFICATION OF INCEST

A spouse's or teenager's accusations of incest can usually be validated with a fair degree of probability if in accord with objective accounts by other family members and confirmed with physical findings. However, the following reservations apply:

Preteenagers may offer lurid stories of incest and illustrate them with genitally equipped "daddy," "mommy," "brother," and "me" dolls, yet furnish questionable versions prompted by prejudiced interviewers, resentments of nonsexual abuse, or misleading television viewings.

In the experience of one of us (JHM) a *folie a deux* involved a father and a 12-year-old daughter so intensely attracted to each other that both participated in a fantasy of erotic relationships during a period when they could not have occurred.

Hostile spouses may allege incest as a reason for divorce (Case 14), punitive alimony, and exclusive custody of the children.

Vaginal, anal, or oral sexual injuries are presumptive but not proof of incestuous intercourse,[2] since they may have been acquired outside the family, but attributed to parent or sibling for various reasons as indicated above.

In effect, in instances of alleged incest, accounts had best be supplemented by psychologic tests and physical findings; even then, inferences should be stated as to degrees of probability rather than as firm conclusions.

CONTINGENT CLINICAL PROCEDURES

These vary as follows:

1. If a father, fearing that recently instituted and still covert sexual relations with a daughter or a son will eventually cause serious complications, seeks individual counselling, the therapist may well be inclined to maintain confidentiality and to provide therapy on the proviso:

(a) That incest cease while the father's personality difficulties are clarified;

(b) That the father follow guidance as to how to rehabilitate his deviated relationships with his daughter or son so as to minimize any trauma they may have experienced;

(c) That if the father is unsuccessful in the latter role, the involved teenager be brought for the alleviation of intercurrent fear and anxiety, and for the correction of any complicating hostile, seductive, pre-emptive, or other adverse traits; and

(d) That the suspicious spouse may also need counselling as to improved domestic relationships, without any unnecessary revelation of the past occurrence of incest.

2. If a distressed mother brings an allegedly victimized child (usually a teenage girl) for guidance as to how to proceed, the first objective is to determine whether incest actually occurred.

(a) If a thorough investigation indicates that it did not, counselling can be devoted to clarifying the serious consequences of false accusations while eliciting and resolving the underlying family conflicts (Case 7).

(b) When incest very probably occurred, the therapist has these options:

  (1) If the incident is reported as legally required, the family is immediately involved in often highly traumatic and disruptive police procedures; if no report is made, the therapist may be held personally liable.

  (2) If the therapist infers that the problem could be resolved, he or she may assume the legal risk leavened by a plea of professional confidentiality, institute intensive individual and joint therapies, and possibly or probably serve the best interest of all concerned.

  (3) However, if the data indicate that the incestuous offender is characterologically impaired (Case 14), chronically disinhibited

by alcohol or drugs, and especially prone to violence when crossed, the case is reported with, when necessary, a request for police protection of the family (and, when indicated, of the therapist). The family may then require skillful guidance through the difficult times ahead.

3. The judge of a juvenile or criminal court may refer the participants in an incestuous relationship for these purposes:

(a) To counsel the teenager and/or the family as to minimizing the presumably deleterious effects of their experiences with domestic incest;

(b) To act as *amicus curiae* (friend of the Court) and advise the judge as to:

(1) Whether the parent was, in legal parlance "insane at the time of the crime and therefore not responsible for his actions." This poses another dilemma: If the examiner does find indications of psychosis, the parent is technically absolved, but the family faces the necessity of hospitalizing him, the supposed onus of "hereditary mental disease" in his children, and other serious problems. If the examiner reports that the parent, in court lexicon, "was aware of the nature and consequences of his acts," the parent may be found "guilty as charged" and face a mandatory prison sentence, again, with devastating effects on the family. If, as a third option, the examiner avoids such legal parlance on the plea that a valid psychiatric diagnosis must take into account many contingent and transitional concepts between the often misleading distinctions of "sane" and "insane," the judge may either select a consultant less troubled by simplistic nosologic dichotomies, or preferably permit the current examiner to present a comprehensive personality appraisal of the offending parent at the trial, thus advancing the cause of justice and that of a sane psychiatry.

(2) In the latter case, if the parent is found guilty but not subject to mandatory imprisonment, the judge may make parole on a suspended sentence, contingent on the parent undertaking reparative counselling. The therapist may accept the assignment, preferably with the proviso that therapy include the abused adolescent, and that a court officer or social worker

rather than the therapist be responsible for reporting any transgressions of the conditions of parole.

TREATMENT OF INCEST

As a general principle, the therapist should not permit his own moral and juristic convictions prejudice his understanding of, empathy with, and treatment of those involved in incest. For adults, appropriately individualized techniques may follow those outlined in Chapter 6; for adolescents, the modalities may be modified as described in the succeeding sections of that Chapter. Municipal social work agencies or Legal Aid Offices may provide special help to indigent patients and families, and "Alcoholics Anonymous" or similar organizations for drug addicts, divorcees, parolees, et al. may offer corresponding group therapies. Throughout, however, it may be wise to apply the precept that the unnecessary induction of familial, social, and legal turmoil may be more traumatic to all concerned than the incest *per se,* and that therefore the quietest, most reassuring and most rehabilitative procedures are to be preferred.

ENDNOTES

1. Nevertheless, the *Old Testament* records several instances of incest long after Adam and Eve: both of Lot's virgin daughters plied him with wine until they could seduce him "to bear his seed." Saul acquired a harem with little regard for consanguinity; Ammon, son of David, raped his sister Tamar while cold sober.

2. However, the genetic detection of a family member's sperm is definitive.

RECOMMENDED READING

Courtois, C.A.: *Healing the Incest Wound.* New York, W.W. Norton, 1988.

Finkelhor, D.: *Child Sexual Abuse.* New York, Free Press, 1984.

Freud, S.: *Totem and Taboo* (1912–13). In Strachey, J. (Ed.): *Standard Edition of the Works of Sigmund Freud,* London, Hogarth Press, 1955, vol. 13.

Henderson, J.: Incest. In Sadock, B., Kaplan, H., Freedman, A. (Eds): *The Sexual Experience.* Baltimore, Williams & Wilkins, 1976.

Kempe, R.S., Kempe, C.H.: *Sexual Abuse of Children and Adolescents.* New York, W.H. Freeman, 1984.

Renshaw, D.: *Incest.* Boston, Little, Brown, 1982.

Chapter 9

DRUGS AND SEXUALITY

With varying concepts of "drug abuse," most observers estimate that of every ten adolescents, five to seven boys and three to five girls have had extended experiences with illegal substances. In general, alcohol, "psychedelics" such as marijuana, LSD, and PCB, and/or narcotics (cocaine, opiates) modify consciousness as an escape from reality. The side-effects sought are feelings of well-being (euphoria), release of fantasies vivified by illusions or hallucinations, sometimes leading to dangerously delusional conduct. Concurrently, there is a diminution of sexual restraints, even though nearly all the drugs used (including the amphetamines, miscalled "uppers") actually diminish libidinal potency.

ALCOHOL[1]

Alcohol has recently taken primacy over other drugs among adolescents for various reasons, among them, that it is usually and inexpensively available at home and arguably in accord with parental patterns. There has been a shift from strong drinks to beers and wines, but many of these contain aromatic ethers and toxic oils especially damaging to young livers, kidneys, and nerves.

Treatment

When a teenager's alcoholism has become a serious problem, therapy, as outlined in Chapter 6 should be based on initial family conferences devoted not to shrill condemnations, but to sympathetic understandings of the possible reasons for the adolescent's drinking, clarification of dangers to his or her health, accomplishments and personal freedom[2] and, when indicated, the advisability of individual counselling. This will consist of a more thorough elucidation of the adolescent's contributory familial, school, peer, sexual, and other difficulties, supplemented when indicated by the prescription of an inhibiting drug (Antabuse® or

Stopethyl®) which, if taken morning or evening under supervision, would cause palpitations, flushings, dizziness, faintness, vomiting and other highly unpleasant somatic reactions if alcohol is ingested during the next three days; even one test of these effects, though convincing, should therefore, be warned against. However, when alcohol and drug combinations cause a dangerous toxic state characterized by terrifying hallucinations and delusions and severe agititation (delerium tremens), hospitalization for emergency treatment becomes imperative.

PSYCHEDELICS

Marijuana

Marijuana ("pot," "grass," "hashish") when used in mild doses, produces a relatively brief period of relaxation and well-being, often followed by some degree of confusion, anxiety and restlessness. Higher doses induce prolonged dream-like impairments of concentration, memory, and speech, with distorted concepts of reality.[3] (One of us was seriously warned by his flying instructor that if he (JHM) "were ever to smoke a single reefer," he must not, on risk of suicide, pilot a plane for at least the next 48 hours.)

LSD

Lysergic acid diethylamide, a chemical produced by a fungus called ergot, when taken even in a minute dose (25 to 150 millionths of a gram) on blotter paper, gelatin squares, or in sugar pills, causes two to 10 hours of impaired perception of time and space, bizarre fantasies, and hallucinatory and delusional experiences; "bad trips" mounting to panic with homicidal and suicidal propensities may be followed after days and months by "flashbacks" that may recall these harrowing effects.[4] Similar compounds such as mescaline (from peyote) and psilocybin (from mushrooms), DMT (from desert shrubs), or related synthetics are still used, often by a regressively "drop out" generation seeking perverse experiences. When these drugs and those described below are abused, vagrancy, seduction, venereal infection, prostitution, imprisonment, etc. are serious consequences.

NARCOTICS

Cocaine

Five centuries ago, slaves of the Incas of Peru learned to chew the leaves of a wild shrub *erythroxyio coca* to relieve the hunger, exhaustion, and misery of their lives. Since then, the coca plant has been extensively cultivated and its leaves extracted to produce cocaine, a product distributed by international crime organizations to enslave millions of addicts worldwide. An especially toxic compound of cocaine called "crack" is now readily available and relatively cheap (as low as "$4 a fix") to produce an instant euphoria, unfortunately followed by physiologic cravings (sweating, cramps, breathing irregularities, anxiety) so intense that many victimized adolescents, particularly in deprived ethnic and racial groups, will beg, lie, cheat, rob, prostitute themselves, or commit assault to secure another supply.

Diagnosis

A careful history and physical examination (sample findings, nasal congestion or perforation from cocaine inhalations, needle scars from injections into arm or leg veins), and/or laboratory tests of blood or urine will reveal cocaine or combined addictions to morphine, barbiturates, amphetamines, or other drugs.

Treatment

Individual. Controversies continue as to whether the infrequent inhalation or other self-administration of cocaine by responsible adults should continue to be illegal; however, there can be no rational objection to protecting teenagers from its deleterious sexual and social effects, especially dangerous when injected ("mainlined") intravenously. Regrettably, there are at present no medicaments, as in opiate addiction, that prevent, meliorate or counteract cocaine addiction, leaving hospitalization as the only alternatives to control the physiologic crises by graduated sedation and withdrawal, followed by the environmental, psychologic, and social modalities of therapy outlined in Chapter 6.

Global. As with marijuana, police methods have to date failed to control the production, distribution, and sale of cocaine and will continue to fail until the criminal cartels are eliminated by concerted international action, including ruthless military measures in what may be called a war to rescue large segments of humanity.

Morphine

This addictive drug is derived from an excretion of the poppy *papaver somniferum* (Latin: "inducer of sleep") which, for centuries had been used medically to relieve pain and promote relaxation and rest.[5] Alkaloids such as codeine, dilaudid, Darvon®, and Demerol®, are less addictive than morphine and, therefore, continue to be prescribed for medical or surgical patients in accord with federal antinarcotic regulations. However, despite the competing popularity of cocaine, morphine and an even more addictive derivative called heroin have also been criminally exploited to ensnare millions of addicts, among them a devastating number of naive and vulnerable teenagers, often recruited from adverse environments for sexual and criminal purposes.

Treatment

Medical measures to free an adolescent from opiate intake may take the following forms:

Outpatient. Without initial hospitalization, the adolescent may be treated at a certified clinic by methadone substitution (see below), or by various antiaddictive drugs (narcotic antagonists such as Cyclazocine®, Naloxone®, or Naltrexone® for milder side-effects) which, if taken daily, are used to diminish or alleviate the previously desired experiences with opiates.

Hospitalization. This may be for the purpose of "cold turkey withdrawal" during which the addict's reactions to total deprivation (yawning, sweating, muscular twitchings, abdominal cramps, vomiting, and diarrhea accompanied by anxiety, rage or depression, only partially relieved by barbiturate or propanolol medication) are allowed to reach a peak in two or three days and then subside. The form of treatment, although a memorable deterrent, is dangerous to physically impaired teenagers and is infrequently used.

Alternatively, while heroin or other opiates are gradually discontinued, the adolescent is placed on substitutive doses of methadone, a less addictive narcotic, which in turn can be more easily withdrawn and the patient discharged either opiate-free or on minimal maintenance doses of methadone.

Unfortunately, all of these medical modalities have serious drawbacks: methadone, even when carefully supervised, merely substitutes one addiction for another and can be correspondingly abused; alternatively, the addict can stop antagonist medication at any time and resume injections of heroin. Statistics as to abstinence and social rehabilitation through the use of antiopiate drugs alone are therefore not encouraging.

Psychotherapy

This should combine dyadic, familial, and group modalities. The latter may include special sessions of supportive organizations called Addicts Anonymous (Synanon, and others), during which adolescents are addressed by ex-addicts about their harrowing past, followed by individual counselling (Chapter 6).

Preventive

All of the above measures, including global police action against criminal cartels, must be supplemented by intensive educational campaigns effectively designed to warn adolescents as to the physical, psychological, and social dangers of all drug addictions.

ENDNOTES

1. One of us (JHM) experimentally clarified the relationship of alcohol to "neurotic" behavior by subjecting monkeys to adaptational conflicts that induced various inhibitions, phobias, and regressions, and demonstrated that, whereas the animals had previously refused alcoholic drinks, most now became addicted to them as sources of relief.

2. Alcohol is easily and embarrassingly detectable in an adolescent's breath or blood after a driving accident or other transgression.

3. The active chemical in these and related plant extracts is delta-9 tetrahydrocannabinol, which can be synthesized or converted to even more dangerous compounds. Frequent inhalations are carcinogenic.

4. LSD was for a time thought by some psychoanalysts to be a useful adjunct to "free association fantasy therapy," a technique now virtually abandoned.

5. These effects parallel the action of natural substances called enkaphalins secreted in the brains of persons under stress.

RECOMMENDED READING

APA Commission on Psychiatric Therapies: *Psychiatric Therapies.* Washington, D.C., American Psychiatric Association, 1984, pp. 277–295.

Dylens, J.W., Niswander, G.D.: The treatment of drug addictions. In Wolman, B. (Ed.): *The Therapist's Handbook.* New York, Van Nostrand, 1976, pp. 430–442.

Illinois Department of Substance Abuse Pamphlet S-2#19, 1989.

Masserman, J.H.: *Behavior and Neurosis.* Chicago, University of Chicago Press, 1943; *Principles of Dynamic Psychiatry.* Philadelphia, W.B. Saunders, 1946.

Wolberg, L.: *Techniques of Psychotherapy.* 3rd Edition. New York, Grune and Stratton, 1977, pp. 802–894.

Chapter 10

SEXUALITY AND SUICIDE

Gestures toward or attempts at suicide, many of which are sexually related, seriously disrupt the normal course of adolescence and, even apart from the tragedies of lethality, require special consideration.

DYNAMICS OF SUICIDE

To begin with a paradox, no one can really imagine the end of his or her own being, since no one can conceive what one has never experienced.[1] We have all slept, or been anesthetized, or even been subject to perhaps epileptic or traumatic comas, yet we have always reawakened to conscious life. "Suicide," then, may be thought of, not as an act of self-annihilation but as an escape, however illusory, from intolerable pain and sorrow to a less-troubled existence.

Incidence

This cannot be accurately determined by the number of certified suicides per year: about two per 100,000 deaths in the United States, nearly half in teenagers.[2] Such statistics would exclude the uncountable instances of despondent human beings of all ages who, with or without lethal doses of alcohol or drugs, deliberately or "accidentally" drive into trees or off cliffs, or are found floating lifeless off swimming beaches. It is a fair estimate that suicide, next to accidental traumata, is most often the cause of death among teenagers, with a frequency reportedly doubled in the last decade.

Familial Influences

Because teenage suicides vary directly with familial incidence (whether genetic, cultural, or exemplary), and occur increasingly in succeeding generations, the following vectors are relevant:

57

Occupations. Highest among dentists, physicians, police and military personnel.

Economic. Highest among the very poor or very rich.

Religion. Forbidden among Jews,[3] and a mortal sin in Christianity and Islam. However, in Nipponese tradition, *hara-kiri*, or *seppuku* (disemboweling), may still be regarded as a commendable personal protest, and *kamikaze* as an act of sublime patriotism to be rewarded by eternal life in a Shinto version of Nirvana.[4]

Country. Highest in Scandinavian countries, lowest in Italy, with other Europeans in between.

Season. Highest in spring and winter.

Urban. Highest in cities, especially those on coasts and mountains.

Race. Three times more frequent in Caucasians than among persons of African descent.

Sex. Three times more frequent in males, except in the Far East.

Age. Highest in teenagers and adults over 55.

PREDISPOSING VECTORS IN ADOLESCENT SUICIDE

Teenagers are in increased jeopardy if subjected to neglect, poverty, physical or emotional abuse, or parental violence and separation, without compensatory sources of security; suicide may then appear to be additionally attractive as an unpunishable revenge on those who made life intolerable. The key elements of *hopelessness* and *alienation* may be illustrated in various combinations by the following examples:

Physical

A 12-year-old boy, suffering the increasing discomforts of cystic fibrosis, learns its inevitable prognosis and decides on an escape he can control.

Familial

A 14-year-old girl, exceedingly dependent on her fanatically religious and punitive parents, decides on suicide to save her family from disgrace when her pregnancy becomes evident.

Failures

Since contentment throughout life is not measured by one's level of possessions or accomplishment, but only as these correspond to what one desires and expects,[5] an adolescent with no other attainments who also fails as a high school quarterback, or a girl not given a cherished role in the senior play, may seriously consider suicide, especially if she was then discarded by her only sex partner in favor of a rival who did succeed.

There is little need to multiply examples; a seeming infinity of stresses adequately coped with in adulthood may be felt as excruciating to the point of desperation by insecure and hypersensitive adolescents.

Signs of Suicidal Intent

These include impairments of appetite, strength, and weight, chronically restless sleep, melancholic preoccupations, crying spells, and other manifestations of a severe depression. Verbal communications may almost cease, or be limited to bitter complaints and outbursts of rage about parental, school, or other injustices. Especially ominous are a loss of previous interests interspersed with episodes of frenetic activity and gifts of previously cherished possessions to selected siblings and friends.

Prevention of Suicide Attempts

Every effort must be made by the parents, and everyone else concerned, preferably with professional help, to determine and relieve the physical or emotional stresses that the adolescent feels as overwhelming. Once sensed, these require not only skillful counselling, but often also active intercessions to resolve familial conflicts, school, peer, or sexual difficulties, or legal liabilities. If these measures prove inadequate, hospitalization is imperative.

TREATMENT OF A SUICIDE ATTEMPT

Immediate

Emergency efforts to neutralize poisoning and control bleeding or choking should not delay urgent arrangements for transporting the adolescent under transient care to a clinic especially equipped to treat suicidal patients. He or she should be accompanied by a responsible family member, who should take along whatever medicaments or instruments were used in the attempt at suicide, and be prepared to give a coherent account of the occurrence. The adolescent should not be permitted to leave the hospital until that is advised by medical and psychiatric professionals, who may also counsel, supplemented by a court order if necessary, individual and familial therapy.

Follow-Up

The event, though inevitably memorable, should not be overdramatized: publicity should be avoided, and legal complications minimized insofar as possible. The goal of individual therapy should be to prevent a recurrence of suicidal gestures by improving the physical well-being, emotional balance, and interpersonal relationships of the troubled adolescent.

THE FAMILY OF A SUICIDE

Treatment

This may be directed toward the resolution of familial stresses, the gradual assuagements of guilts, a redirection of concerns toward surviving siblings and a rationally-paced resumption of previous social interests and activities.

Global. Millions of our youth are now living in an overcrowded world of anomie, poverty, hunger, pollution, disease, increasingly paranoid conflicts, and a constant threat of additional chemically- and/or atomically-induced suffering from which suicide may seem to be an attractive escape. The actions required of all informed and intelligent adults transcend local and cultural boundaries, and may indeed be termed individually, socially, and existentially (Ur-) urgent on a global scale. The concerted modalities to be employed have been described by one of us (JHM) in a series of articles listed under Recommended Reading.

ENDNOTES

1. True, no one has ever confronted a fire-breathing dragon, but we can easily magnify the image of a salamander, equip it with bat's wings and shark's teeth, and endow it with internal combustion expelled through a flaming snout; so also can we combine previous items of experience into visualizing a transparent Martian with cerebral antennae, seven death-ray eyes and wheeled locomotion. Such creatures, too, could be killed as "we" have killed others, *but no one has ever killed "me."*

2. Teenagers prefer drugs or auto exhausts, whereas a bullet to the brain or heart is the method used in more than half of adult suicides. Others at higher economic levels may elect to die more "heroically" by sailing their racing sloops into hurricanes or having their engines fail unaccountably in their private planes during a final flight heavenward.

3. Nevertheless, Saul committed suicide to escape his captors, and the Old Testament approved Samson's self-immolation in bringing down an idolatrous temple on Delilah and the Philistines.

4. Other fantasies include earthly reincarnations in a merited Brahmian progression toward perfect serenity (*karma*), rejoining lost loved ones in heaven, or being elevated to angelic or even saintly status—all, incidentally, devoid of the strains of sexuality.

5. A Baconian aphorism revised for therapeutic use by Adolf Meyer, who long ago taught it to one of us (JHM).

RECOMMENDED READING

Durkheim, E.: *Suicide.* Glencoe, Illinois, Free Press, 1951.

Haim, A.: *Adolescent Suicide.* New York, International Universities Press, 1970.

Masserman, J.H.: Or shall we all commit suicide? In Masserman, J.H. (Ed.): *Current Psychiatric Therapies.* New York, Grune and Stratton, 1962, vol. 2, pp. 273–278.

Masserman, J.H.: Transcultural anxieties and social therapies. In Masserman, J.H. (Ed.): *Current Psychiatric Therapies.* New York, Grune and Stratton, 1983, vol. 22, pp. 257–266.

Pfeffer, C.: *The Suicidal Child.* New York, Guilford, 1986.

Schwab, J.J. and Schwab, M.: *Sociocultural Roots of Mental Illness.* New York, Plenum, 1978.

Chapter 11

CASE ILLUSTRATIONS

These case vignettes are arranged in accord with the functions of the specialist in adolescent behavior, not only as diagnostician and therapist, but also as peer reviewer and forensic consultant. The case numbers correspond to those in the relevant chapters.

INDIVIDUAL AND FAMILY THERAPIES

Case 1. Adolescent Dysphoria

A therapist who specializes in problems of adolescence is frequently called upon to supervise the therapy of a patient hospitalized by a colleague in another specialty. The following is an instance of maintained confidentiality.

Medical Review

S, age 16, was admitted to the orthopedic service with complaints of back pains since a "basketball fall" two months previously, exacerbated three weeks later by another injury "while wrestling with her older sister." Her pains had become severe and constant, had spread to her thighs and lower ribs, and had necessitated nightly doses of Somnifen® for sleep. Other symptoms included headaches, dysmenorrhea, dysuria, and "general nervousness." Physical, laboratory studies, and an x-ray of the pelvis and spine had revealed no abnormal findings.

Supplementary Anamnesis

S was interviewed in an orthopedic examining room where she was assured of privacy. In elaborating her complaints, S also reported recurrent episodes of palpitation, globus, dyspnea, and trembling accompanied by intense apprehensions that "people were talking" about her. The family history was contributory only in that the patient's father was described as "a nervous invalid," some of whose symptoms the patient seemed to have adopted, whereas her mother was characterized as "weak, fussy, and jealous of me because I'm my father's favorite."

With rapport increasingly established on the grounds of continued confidentially, S related that her father had become "enraged" that she had hurt her back by disobeying his orders not to play "dangerous basketball," but had relented and resumed his indulgences when she became further "disabled" after playful wrestling with her sister. S then confessed that her back injury had actually occurred during some strenuous coital activities with her "steady" in the constricted front seat of his ancient coupe. After a second such exacerbation, she had been fearful that her parents would learn the real cause of her pains, and that "everyone in town" would suspect that her limping was due to a "sex disease." Her father's insistence that she be treated in the hospital had increased her concerns, since a venereal disease or even an early pregnancy might be revealed.

Psychologic

S's intelligence was average and her sensorium clear, although affected by pervasive anxieties. As empathy progressed, she began to regard the consultant as a paternal surrogate, and accepted explanations that most of her symptoms were due to "nervous reactions" to her recent emotional as well as physical stresses; she then offered to cooperate in psychotherapy if her parents were told only that her symptoms were due solely to some "basketball strains in my back and muscles which just need some pills."

Summary of Conjoint Therapy

The therapist informed S that his review of her physical and laboratory findings showed unequivocally that she was neither pregnant nor venereally infected; however, he agreed with her that she needed sympathetic treatment and confidential guidance. In a subsequent interview S's orthopedic physician, without mentioning the psychiatric consultation, informed S's parents in her presence that her x-rays, myograms, etc., had revealed no evidence of bone or nerve injury, and that her medical examination had indicated that her cardiac and respiratory complaints, as well as her back pains, had been due to muscle tensions, which were frequent in sensitive and conscientious youngsters, usually overconcerned about their school work. Small doses of Motrin® and "relaxing exercises" were prescribed, and S was discharged for further care specifically to the outpatient orthopedic clinic.

There, a young female trainee in psychiatry, assigned in liaison to orthopedics, counselled S as to

a) more mutually productive familial relationships, especially with her father and sister, and b) the advisability of chastity until S reached greater maturity or, failing that, c) more reasonable choices of partner and place for her premature and precarious erotic adventures.

Of the three, S professed to choose family amity and "much better" sexual restraint, rationalizing the latter choice by recalling that D, her boyfriend, "didn't stand by when I was in trouble" and that in her experience, "the boys I knew were big-shot jerks" best avoided anyway.

After two weekly sessions S discontinued her placebo medication, and at a third, reported family peace, and that she was doing well in school. In a fourth and final session attended by her father both declared that she was symptom free and not in need of additional visits.

There was no follow-up as to long-term results. (JHM)

Case 2. Hormonal Deficiency

An adolescent had been treated by a nonmedical psychoanalyst for a year for sexual dysfunctions and "emotional distress" without improvement. Physical and laboratory findings indicated low thyroid function, and medical treatment proved effective.

R, 17, complained of oral numbness, tingling of the fingers, easy fatiguability, lack of sexual desire, and depression. Further inquiries revealed that during the past three years R had also suffered headaches, constipation, an excessive gain in weight despite a decreased appetite, irregular menstrual bleeding, and a marked sensitivity to cold. The psychoanalyst had attributed her somatic difficulties and self-isolation to an "unresolved Electra complex"; this had "clarified" her depression, but she continued to suffer from decreased energy and lack of libido. A "sex therapist" had recommended self-stimulations of breasts and clitoris accompanied by erotic fantasies, but this had increased her anxieties.

Psychologic

R manifested forgetfulness of names and dates, sensations "as if I were someone else," and dull affect, all of which she still attributed to "unconscious complexes."

Physical examination

Positive findings included a slow pulse, puffiness of face and eyelids, sparse hair, dry skin, broken nails, and hand paresthesias suggestive of a carpal syndrome.

Therapy

Hypothyroidism was diagnosed and R was referred to an endocrinologist for hormonal therapy. At a follow-up interview four months later, she was dating, her "neurotic depression and anxiety" had been alleviated and, although she was still not sexually active, she was experiencing libidinal arousals. (VMU)

Case 3. Coital Dysfunctions

Present Problems

G, age 18, reported that he had always been capable of strong penile erections before and for two months after he married M. However, a month earlier and at his insistence, they had practiced fellatio and cunnilingus for the first time, and when he had then attempted vaginal intromission in the female-superior position his phallus became flaccid. He had reacted with anxiety but, in response to his wife's reassurances and caresses, had continued to respond to mutual foreplay with an erection; nevertheless, vaginal penetration again failed, as it has ever since. Despite assertions of mutual love, G had become increasingly concerned about "not being manly," whereas his wife has been troubled about being "a bad sexual partner." Both had also felt perverted and depressed about their "dirty" sexual activities.

Therapy

In response to empathetic reassurances as to the normality of their erotic explorations, the couple rapidly developed a therapeutic rapport. Reorientations focused on their misconceptions as to foreplay and varied coital modalities. It was pointed out that since G had strong erections, he was not "impotent," and that cunnilingus and fellatio were common sex practices between consenting partners. The sex manuals listed in Chapter 7 were recommended, and the couple was referred for supplementary counseling as to their religious concerns. G readily resolved his self-doubts and M her conflicts about varied sexuality.

After two individual weekly sessions, three joint sessions, and one a month later for follow-up, mutual marital satisfactions were restored. (VMU)

Case 4. Impotence

J, an 18-year-old college student, complained of losing erection before vaginal penetration, general "nervousness," and fears of being "homosexual."

Anamnesis

From three to eight years of age, J and a sister two years older had fondled each other's genitals while bathing together, or when playing house and nurse-and-doctor games. From age 10 to 12, he and his sister "necked and petted," while he masturbated. On one occasion he had tried vaginal intercourse with her but when she struck away his penis, it "had dropped dead." They had then stopped their erotic explorations; instead, he had masturbated more frequently and had indulged in pornographic magazines, home X-rated movies, and erotic talk with other adolescents. He continued to fantasize "feeling up" girls, but always stopped short of imagining vaginal penetration, because this precipitated "nervousness" and "fears."

When a high school senior, to conform with peer pressure, and to relieve his gender anxieties, he began to date, but whenever he tried vaginal intromission his penis again "dropped dead." He had therefore begun to think of himself "as a girl" who needed pampering and nurturing, with sporadic fears of being a "homosexual," "degenerate," or "pervert."

Summary of Treatment

Initial resistances were relieved by a mild tranquilizer for anxiety and insomnia, and empathetic reassurances that therapy could resolve his sexual problems. Nevertheless, for several sessions, as he associated his current impotence to the incident with his older sister, he became breathless, tense, and fearful, and in a trembling voice again insisted that he had "just played games," and had therefore felt justified in having been angry about his sister's rejection. For several more sessions he remained unaware of his concurrent resentment of the therapist for having evoked these trepidations. When this appeared unmistakeably in J's associations and vivid dreams, he traced his explicit fears of castration, femininity, and homosexuality to his strict religious upbringing. He then requested that the therapist's reassurances be supplemented by religious advice, and was referred to a minister known by the therapist to be kindly and helpful. Under this joint counselling, J's concerns about his "cardinal sin" of attempted incest with his sister abated, yet he remained unable to attain vaginal intercourse even with a specially permissive girl. Exercises in progressive sexual techniques (see Recommended Readings, Chapter 7) for premature ejaculation were practiced by the couple. After three months of simultaneous weekly sessions J, now a freshman at college, declared himself potent and happy with his mistress. (VMU)

Case 5. Incompatibility

The therapist may encounter difficulties in overcoming cultural and religious factors in the therapy of sexual incompatibility.

Presenting Complaints

R, 19, had experienced premature ejaculations, and his wife C, 17, had been "frigid" since their marriage three months earlier.

C's Anamnesis

C's immediate and extended families included priests and nuns, and she had received a traditional Catholic upbringing. C therefore felt intense inhibitions about sexuality, although she knew her father had kept mistresses. In secret explorations, she had tried stimulating her breasts and vulva, but had felt "weird, dirty, sinful" as soon as she became vaginally aroused. After marriage she had consented to intercourse only in the male-superior position, and had welcomed premature ejaculations to relieve her lack of vaginal lubrication. At R's insistence, the couple had tried various practices illustrated in a sex manual, but C had frequently objected because prolonged physical foreplay or sustained thrusting aroused guilt and anxiety.

R's Anamnesis

R stated that "he was also a Catholic, but just as a believer" and therefore had an active sexual life premaritally. In C's presence R said that her lack of orgastic response "did not bother" him, but he later confided being sexually dissatisfied with his wife. To overcome his premature ejaculation during unsatisfactory intercourse with her, R had tried many methods: precoital cocktails or sedatives, anesthetizing his penis with ointments, attending to nonerotic objects, and self-inflicted pain. All had been unsuccessful, and he feared that he would become totally impotent.

Therapy

In view of C's religious preoccupations, the couple was advised to consult a Catholic priest regarding her conflicts about marital sexuality.

R was advised to stop his ineffectual precoital stimulations; instead, after applying the progressive sex techniques (see Chapter 7, Recommended Reading) he was able to delay his orgasm, even though C declined to perform penile pressures or coitus in any but male superior position.

The treatment of C's lack of orgastic response was then intensified. In collaboration with her pastoral counsellor, reeducation focused on misconceptions as to normal and permissable marital sexual responses free of overscrupulous religious inhibitions. However, even after 20 office consultations supplemented by priestly counsel and specially prescribed sex exercises, she remained anorgastic.

The couple was therefore advised either to explore and resolve the increasingly obvious marital conflicts that underlay their remaining sexual difficulties or to accept their current compromises. They chose the latter and discontinued therapy. (VMU)

Case 6. Sexuality in Depression

The therapy of sexual dysfunction may require relief of a concurrent depression.

Presenting Complaint

F, 18, and P, 17, reported having been "happy with each other" and sexually compatible after their engagement nine months earlier; however, they were now mutually irritable and uncertain about their relationship. They had planned to marry within a year, but were "having second thoughts." For the past three months their trials of diverse sexual practices had become progressively more troubled, and they now needed "sex therapy."

Anamnesis

On detailed inquiry F stated that since losing his job four months earlier, he had been unable to obtain even a promise of another. He had suffered from decreased appetite and energy, a loss of 15 pounds, insomnia, sporadic nightmares of being confined to a "house on fire" or "falling from high heights." He was discouraged and had felt despair about providing for P's and his own future.

Physical and Laboratory

The findings were not contributory.

Diagnosis

Reactive depression and anxiety with secondary sexual dysfunctions.

Therapy

In joint interviews F and P were gently informed that their sex problems were secondary to a loss of faith in each other: F as provider, and P as a prospective wife who, instead of being insensitive to his concerns, would help him sympathetically through troubled periods. F's occupational skills were reviewed and, with increased confidence, he sought reemployment through recommended agencies and within 2 weeks had found suitable work. The couple's interpersonal and sexual relations rapidly improved without other specific therapy and their marriage plans were resumed. (VMU)

Case 7. Alleged Incest: Emergency Family Therapy

Combined individual, familial, social, and juristic therapeutic modalities may be called for in the immediate interests of all concerned.

The Problem

Mr. L Z, age 41, was referred by his firm's medical director for relief of an intense anxiety-depressive state which had seriously interfered with his proficiency as a cost accountant. After assurances of empathy and confidentiality, Mr. Z, a spare, stooped, prematurely aging individual, tendered the following account of his past and current difficulties:

Anamnesis

Raised in a repressively religious but essentially loveless family, Mr. Z had felt isolated and alienated through much of his life, had developed few recreational or esthetic interests, and had concentrated on what he considered his only talent: a ready grasp of mathematics. He had served his present employers well for nearly two decades, but because of his constricted interpersonal relationships had not been promoted to supervisory or managerial positions.

Eleven years earlier, after a characteristically hesitant courtship, he had "married the only girl that I thought might ever want me;" but because of his wife's dissatisfaction with Mr. Z's lack of social graces or economic advancement, the childless marriage ended in two years. Mr. Z then spent another seven years before marrying a divorcee with a 9-year-old daughter, Carol. The second Mrs. Z, too, soon began to treat him with growing indifference and sexual denials, whereas Carol, who had been starved for affection from both her own parents, found her stepfather highly responsive to her needs for affection and care. According to Mr. Z, after he "had helped the child with her homework, she always wanted to sit on my lap and hug me to show me how she loved her new Daddy." Inevitably, as Carol grew older, these contrectations began to acquire repressed erotic undertones and, although they never approached impropriety, they resonated unfortunately with concurrent external events as follows:

The Z's lived in a suburban community which had become greatly concerned over stories in the media about the sexual abuse of children in the homes and schools of the neighboring metropolis. In response to public pressure, the local school board had instituted a program of "preventive education," consisting largely of having the board's psychologist present lectures at the local schools on the sexual mistreatment of children, followed by small group discussions during which the participants were urged to relate their relevant experiences. In one such session Carol, now aged 11, felt she should describe how she "liked to kiss and hug Daddy a lot before he tucked me into bed every night."

Carol's enthusiastic accounts were apparently misinterpreted by the psychologist, who conveyed his suspicions of incest to the school principal, who reported them, apparently with increasing elaboration, to the local sheriff. The latter, with special zeal enhanced by his recently publicized defalcations in office, promptly arrested Mr. Z on charges of contributing to the delinquency of a minor, and kept him imprisoned for two days until a $40,000 bond could be arranged.

Mr. Z engaged a defense attorney, but received scant comfort from the latter's precautionary statements that the county prosecutor, in his campaign for reelection, had vowed that he was intent on "making an example of any sex perverts in this community."

Therapy

My examination of Mr. Z indicated that although he had, indeed, used poor judgment in physically reciprocating Carol's affection, he had actually indulged in no practices that could be termed "sexual abuse." I therefore calmed his fears, prescribed three anxiolytic capsules, and scheduled separate interviews with Mrs. Z and Carol, to be followed by a family session.

Mrs. Z. The second Mrs. Z confided that soon after their marriage she had increasingly resented her husband's social "aloofness, his fussiness, his never getting anywhere at his job, or anywhere else," etc. She had therefore "lost interest in him" in favor of her church work, and, as to his current difficulties, "God will see that he gets whatever he deserves." However, when it was pointed out that Mr. Z's incarceration would entail serious consequences for both herself and Carol, she promised that she "would talk to that silly girl about it and see what she could do."

Carol. Tearful and confused, Carol described how the county prosecutor had audiotaped her account of "how Daddy always hugged and kissed me before putting me to bed." However, though at first defensive and defiant, Carol soon responded to an avuncular approach and listened receptively to the options I outlined for her:

If she did not clarify her story and her stepfather went to jail, she would not only be deprived of his care and support, but would feel that she had sent him there. Also, she might be avoided by classmates as "the daughter of a criminal," be subject to unwanted advances because of her presumed sexual experiences, and suffer other regrets and difficulties. This concerned me as her friend and adviser.

Alternatively, while I could not counsel her to disclaim her recorded testimony (I did not add that this, indeed, might constitute subornation of evidence), she could still inform the prosecuting attorney that if forced to testify she could honestly say, from what she had told me, that she had always welcomed her stepfather's attentions and affection, and had never considered him in any way sexually abusive. Carol agreed that she would "try to do that."

The Family Session. With Mr. Z, his wife, and Carol present, the above issues were reviewed. Mrs. Z, with barely concealed jealousy of her daughter's attractiveness, began to urge her "to straighten out this mess you got us all into," and Carol, crestfallen and contrite, again agreed. Mr. Z, greatly relieved, and with Mrs. Z's reluctant consent, requested a follow-up session, but both, in accord with the ethics of the situation, were referred to a competent family therapist for continuous counselling.

Forensic. On the basis of these interviews, I telephoned Mr. Z's attorney to give him permission to inform the county prosecutor that if Mr. Z were brought to trial, I would testify that, on the basis of my examinations of Mr. Z, Mrs. Z, and Carol, it was my professional judgment that Mr. Z had been a devoted stepparent and had not subjected Carol to sexual abuse.

Follow-Up

Ten days later Mr. Z called to inform me that charges against him had been dropped, that he was now "feeling great, getting along better with Carol, and doing fine at work again." However, while he "had greatly appreciated" my help and could use more advice to prevent another divorce, Mrs. Z wanted him instead "to join her in prayers with her pastor," and he thought it best for marital harmony to do so.

Mr. Z was again cautioned to consult his firm's personnel counselor before rather than after another crisis developed, and to continue therapy if so advised. A month later, his office supervisor reported that Mr. Z's work performance was again satisfactory, and no follow-up occurred. (JHM)

THERAPIST AS PEER REVIEWER

Universities, insurance companies, industrial firms, health maintenance organizations (HMOs), and other agencies frequently request an evaluation of the treatment of a child or adolescent by another therapist, whose reports, with his or her identity deleted, are forwarded to the consultant for a "peer review." The following cases exemplify commentaries on various forms of therapy for preteen and adolescent sexual and other behavior disorders.

Case 8. Adolescent Psychoanalysis

As a trained analyst, one of us was requested to review the treatment of an adolescent girl as summarized in two reports.

Summary of Data Submitted

(Quotes are in the claimant therapist's reports to the insurance agency.)

D, age 13, is described as "extremely aggressive, disruptive, sexually preoccupied, and unable to function adequately despite excellent intellectual endowment."

Anamnesis

Summarized as: "She suffered [unspecified] illnesses before age two, so always needed parental indulgences."

First Report on Therapy. "After 10 months of analytic sessions twice a week the youngster has a good therapeutic regression in which to experience her core personality problems. This middle phase will require 40 more sessions."

Second Report 10 Months Later. "She is more aware of her problems, but continues vulnerable, wants to exhibit her genitals, says she likes being crazy . . . and is still in a therapeutic regression. She will still need about 40 sessions before beginning to deal with separation anxiety."

Reviewer's Evaluation

Because of the cryptic reports and stereotyped formulations, it is difficult to determine if D's family is being consulted as to whether D is actually improving her parental, sibling, school, and other relationships, her flagrant sexuality, and her general delinquency. Since her intensive and unremitting treatment has already lasted nearly two years and is now projected indefinitely, it is justified to require more specific evidence of progress from objective observers. Failing favorable accounts, it may be well to discontinue regressive analytic techniques in favor of realistically guided and rewarding familial, peer, educational, and other resocializing modalities. (JHM)

Case 9. Sexual Delinquency

A review of a request by the staff of a private hospital for the continued institutionalization of an adolescent for another 12 to 18 months occasioned the following commentary on goal-directed therapy versus group diffusion.

Records

P is a 16-year-old girl with a vaguely described history of generalized hostility, truancy, drug abuse, sexual promiscuity, and an aborted pregnancy. As specified in the hospital staff's report, treatment during the previous 14 months of institutionalization had included "daily sessions of individual, group, family, and milieu therapies" conducted by "a multidisciplinary team" whose objectives were "to foster tentative peer relationships . . . class attendance . . . and valuing herself as a person." The "team roster" consisted of "a team leader" [training unspecified], a "consulting psychiatrist, . . . a senior mental health worker [unspecified], a primary mental health worker [unspecified], subsidiary mental health workers [unspecified], a team teacher, and a team nurse." All of these had endeavored to improve P's "object introjects," "primal paranoia," and "transferential acting out;" however, recent notes describe her conduct as frequently more disturbed than on her entry to the hospital.

Reviewer's Evaluation

If necessary, several weeks of intensive institutional therapy for delinquent juveniles can introduce them to individualized guidance and favorably controlled group-reorientative experiences; conversely, longer hospitalization with diffuse and unfocused treatment may be counterproductive by encouraging rebellious, regressive, and socially unrealistic extramural life patterns. The data furnished in this instance yield no basis for affirming (a) that the diverse, prolonged, and expensive modalities employed have been helpful or (b) that their continuation for yet another year would be successful. The hospital could agree to a site visit by one or two experts in adolescent therapy who would review the records in collaboration with the staff, and submit unbiased recommendations as to the optimum modifications of P's current regime. (JHM)

Case 10. A Troubled Uncle

Reports to physician friends who seek professional advice on family affairs may likewise be frank and explicit.

Dear _____:

Your 15-year-old nephew, K N, can be characterized briefly: About as badly spoiled, self-willed, and undisciplined a perennial pubescent as I've had in the office lately. Unfortunately, he has learned all the standard techniques of seducing and controlling his parents, particularly his wishfully gullible mother, and is firmly convinced that these will serve him indefinitely everywhere. Some of his misinterpretations of reality border on the schizoid, but his main patterns of escapism, indulgence, bravado, and explosive aggression when frustrated are sociopathic, but still possibly reversible.

His treatment, directed as much to his family as himself, will have to be along the following lines:

Clear and unequivocal directives to K as to the necessity of major changes in his values, goals, and behavior;

Urgent placation of the father of a neighborhood girl to remove the threat of police action over K's attempt to seduce the father's 12-year-old daughter.

Removal by K of the obscene graffitti he had been caught spraying on walls, postal boxes, and sidewalks;

Supervised discipline of K as to interpersonal decency, school attendance, etc., to be realistically motivated by rewards for improved conduct or inevitable deprivations of privileges for the reverse;

Concurrent family counselling to counter K's predictable maneuvers (appeals, threats, vagrancy, etc.) to vitiate the above;

Failing adequate control at home, recourse to a parochial boarding school or military academy with facilities for imposed discipline not to be parentally countermanded.

During separate conferences with K N and his parents I made the above as plain as I could within the limitations of time and tact, and referred them back to you for further guidance. Without the cooperation of the family, I doubt I can be of further help.

Follow Up

A week later, the avuncular colleague reported that K's mother had indignantly declined to implement any of the above recommendations, and that he had therefore removed himself from surrogate responsibility for K's future. (JHM)

Case 11. Schizoid Disorder

The rehospitalization for continued care of a schizophrenic adolescent with sexual and other problems was endorsed, for actuarial coverage in the following instance.

Summary of Hospital Records

N, a 16-year-old girl hospitalized for fantastic phobias, bizarre religious preoccupations, and recent suicidal gestures.

History. Her father, diagnosed as schizophrenic, had divorced the patient's mother when the patient was four. N's conduct, though never "normal," had been variably dereistic under stresses such as her mother's remarriage, changes of family locale, the birth of a half-sister, and a recently attempted seduction by her stepfather. The patient had been unable to attend school for the six months prior to admission.

Physical and Lab Examinations. Repeatedly within normal limits.

Psychologic. Schizoid, depressive, and religio-dereistic features as indicated, with tangible risks of suicide.

Therapy. Two previous hospitalizations for combined schizoaffective medication elsewhere were only temporarily beneficial. Current therapy includes dyadic, group, educational, and social skill modalities, with suicidal precautions when indicated.

Diagnosis. "Schizophrenia, chronic undifferentiated, with atypical depression 296.82."

Progress. Monthly notes indicate that responses to treatment have been irregular; despite occasional periods of trust and collaboration, N related poorly to staff and peers, and repeatedly transgressed school and ward responsibilities. Following a family visit, N suffered a major psychotic break with confusion, hallucinations, and bizarre behavior. However, with a change of therapist, modification of external demands, and increased Haldol® medication, N has shown cognitive and affective improvement.

Reviewer's Replies to Numbered Queries on the Insurance Form

1. Psychiatric therapy was and is necessary.
2. The educational and rehabilitative programs may be further modi-

fied to keep fantasied stresses within the patient's tolerance, but the hospital care has on the whole been appropriate.

3. Therapy should include a dietary and vitamin regime for underweight, and maintenance phenothiazine or butyrophenon medication.

4–7. Length of stay has been appropriate to date, and staff has indicated adequate understanding and empathy, as exemplified by literate and objective monthly reports.

8. However, the hospital's prognosis of "a long-term stay" should not become a self-fulfilling prophecy for both staff and patient. Institutionalization for not more than six additional months had best be programmed for return to extramural schooling, social rehabilitation, and follow-up for outpatient medication and dyadic and family supervision. (JHM)

THERAPIST AS FORENSIC CONSULTANT

Juvenile Court judges frequently request counsel as to the psychiatric status and optimum disposition of adolescents under their jurisdiction. The following cases are illustrative of the sexually-related problems involved.

Case 12. Exhibitionism in a Pubescent Male

A judge mandated a psychiatric examination for P, age 17, arrested for exposing his genitals.

Presenting Problems

P stated that "every week or so" during the past six months "I showed my pecker to little girls but I didn't do nothing else." After such exposures he had masturbated, "to feel big," but then felt guilty, ashamed, and "lonely." He knew what he did "was wrong but I couldn't help it." His sleep had been troubled by nightmares of falling from heights and awakening only "just before I smashed the ground." He was now afraid of being sent "to an insane hospital" and eventually "to hell."

P stated that his sisters and other female relatives had frequently "fondled" him when he was a child. He recalled that he played nude games with three younger female cousins and enjoyed their excitement whenever he showed them his erect penis. However, seven years ago his father had caught him doing so, spanked him, and made him stop the exhibitions.

P's father died of a cerebral accident at age 55, six months earlier, leaving P anxious and insecure. He continued to live with his diabetic mother, with whom he often feels uncomfortable because she became both overprotective of, and overdependent upon him. Frequently, while caressing him she tells him either "You are my baby," or "You are now the man of the house," requiring him to act in both roles.

Physical Examination

The findings were noncontributory.

Psychologic

P was sad, ashamed, and fearful, but oriented and intelligent. He initially regarded the psychiatrist as a court functionary who would decide to imprison him; however, in response to empathetic reassurance, he developed a tentative rapport and became cooperative.

Summary of the Report to the Juvenile Court

The psychiatrist advised the Court that since P showed no serious personality defects, his recent exhibitionistic reactions to the death of his father could probably be eliminated in outpatient therapy.

Summary of Treatment

In the first interview, the therapist helped P to resolve his initial anxieties and resistances by assuring him that the therapist, as a doctor rather than as a policeman or priest, had no other purpose than to work confidentially with him to understand and resolve his problems. He encouraged P to express his wishes, emotions, and fantasies freely, including his attitudes toward the therapist as reflecting those toward other present and past persons.

In three separate interviews the psychiatrist helped P's mother resolve her possessive and dependent attitudes toward her son after her husband's death. The therapist encouraged her to become involved with part-time business schooling and work that also provided new interests and companionship, thus also aiding in P's emancipation.

P began to understand his exhibitionism as a reaction to his father's death and his mother's conflicting demands. When worries about her diabetes also abated after her internist assured him that her life was not in danger, sedatives to relieve P's insomnia and nightmares were discontinued.

By the 10th session, P's urges to exhibitionism vanished, so that subsequent sessions were devoted to increasing his awareness of the dangers of other expressions of his hostile, grandiose, and domineering impulses.

In response to the therapist's recommendation, the court terminated P's supervised probation. In three follow-up sessions at six-month intervals, P reported that with no relapses of exibitionism, he had established a friendship with a girl near his own age. Two years later, P wrote that he had lived happily with the same girl after his therapy, had married her when she became of age, and that they now had a two-month old daughter. (VMU)

Case 13. Pyromania

Acting as a consultant (amicus curiae) to a judge of a juvenile court, one of us (JHM) interviewed an adolescent who had been arrested for setting a series of fires, and submitted the following findings and recommendations.

To the Honorable _____

In response to your request, herewith a summary of my findings in the case of O M, age 15.

Examination at the County Detention Facility on May 16, 19-

O M was found sitting in his cell neatly dressed, clean, and readily cooperative. Spontaneously or in response to nondirective questions, he gave the following account of his experiences (quotes are in O's words):

Last week he had skipped school and in the afternoon had watched a TV science fiction program depicting how "Alpha Centaury explorers had caught a fire disease that made them start magic fires." After the show, he kept hearing a voice repeat, "fire, fire, fire . . . this made me get some kerosene and some old boxes and pick out any old house and put them beneath the porch and put fire to them so I could smell it." O then went home to wait for the sound of fire engines. When they did not arrive he found other boxes, carried them to the back porch of the house next to his original choice, again poured kerosene on them and set them afire, during all of which time the voice was still repeating, "fire, fire, fire." As he watched the second fire spread, he experienced constricted vision, mounting sexual excitement, and loss of control over his arms and legs, culminating in a genital orgasm.

The next morning he read that a man asleep in the burned house had died of asphyxiation, but felt no contrition; instead, he merely showed the newspaper to his mother and spent the rest of the day again watching horror stories on television. However, that night he felt the need for more erotic gratification; accordingly, he "set a fire I think on M Street or somewhere like that, but it didn't catch." He therefore moved to V Street and set the fourth fire in the series. A half-hour later, while watching the second house in flames, he had "a real good jacking off" and again felt satisfied. On this occasion, however, the police were questioning all loiterers in the neighborhood, and he too was detained until his mother came to his rescue with the alibi that he had been at home until "just a few minutes ago." (At this juncture, O commented: "But she knew I had been setting fires in the basement of my house for the last six months.")

Still troubled by this contact with the police after his return home, he conceived the idea that, in order to divert further suspicion from himself, he should set fire to his own home and pretend that some intruder had done so. He therefore set a few boxes ablaze in his basement, banged a window open and shut, and went to his mother's bedroom with the story that he had seen "someone escaping holding something smoking in his hand."

The fire was easily extinguished, after which he and his mother sat talking and drinking tea until 3 a.m. When she retired, he set a second fire on his own back porch and watched it flare until the house was threatened. He then again called his mother, and went upstairs to get E, his younger brother, out of trouble, "but I was going to let Dad get burned because he was always drinking and he never did nothing for me. Mother kept saying that she was going to leave him but she was sticking it out for me . . . "

Affect

O frequently interspersed the above account with his sexual perversions with various neighborhood girls; with similar indifference, he stated that he would like "to have a rifle to shoot wild things." At no time did O seem to be truly cognizant of, or correspondingly troubled by, the seriousness or significance of his actions.

Supplementary Office Interview with O's Mother

Mrs. M took out prepared notes and began to defend her son. She stated that when he was only 5 years old he plugged in an iron and set fire to the sofa; at 6½ he was repeatedly reprimanded by the teacher for bringing matches to school. At the age of six he put ashes in his baby brother's eyes and explained this on the grounds that he "was no longer of any account since the baby was born." At nine he began walking off from his playmates in the midst of a game. (When the mother was asked at this point as to when she wrote the notes to which she repeatedly referred, she replied "ten days ago for my lawyer.") She then continued as follows: O's father "had fixed the basement up for the boy," but had "turned drunkard and not played with him much" and O had resented this deeply. At 12, O was expelled from high school because of destructive aggressiveness and intolerable mischief; he was also stealing money from his father while letting the family want for food.

Impression

A maternally protective defense of O, nevertheless indicative of his dereistic and lifelong antisocial characteristics.

Assessment

In our currently ambiguous psychiatric nosology, O could be diagnosed either as an erotically perverse "juvenile pyromaniac" responsible for his acts, or as a "schizophrenic" adolescent. In the latter case, by the M'Naughten, New Hampshire or ABA criteria of psychopathy, he would be considered not culpable since, although he knew the consequences of his acts and wished to escape detection and punishment he was "morally indifferent as to right or wrong" and therefore had "felt no guilt" about his behavior, however bizarre and dangerous.

The district attorney may well marshall professional opinion for the first diagnosis. If O is then found "sane" and guilty of arson on trial, permit me to recommend that, instead of confining him to the counterproductive rigors and erotic dangers of an adult prison with few facilities for rehabilitating juveniles, O instead be sent to a maximal security Audie Home for psychiatric therapy until certified as capable of release on parole for continued outpatient treatment and supervision.

Follow-Up

With the cooperation of a capable defense attorney engaged by Mrs. M, a feasible compromise was reached by having O "voluntarily" enter a psychiatric hospital with far better provisions for his treatment than would have been found in the state prison. (JHM)

Case 14. Judgment on a Sex Offender

Even when sexual abuse has been established, a legal disposition best for the adolescent, the offender, and their respective families should be carefully considered. Herewith a representative report.

To the Honorable _____

In response to your directive on joint petitions of District Attorney A H, vs. Mr. J L for the defense, herewith my report on E W, arrested on May 6, 19____ on charges of contributing to the delinquency of a minor.

Examination

E W, age 19, stated that while driving a school bus at about 5:30 p.m. on May 4 he picked up a male teenager who requested a ride and drove him along the bus route for about 20 minutes. During this time they "talked about girls," whereupon E W, allegedly by invitation, palpated the boy's penis through his clothes and caused him to have two ejaculations. After the second of these the youngster grew angry, left the bus, threw a stone at it, and ran off. Two days later, on complaint of the boy's parents, E W was arrested on charges of child molestation and imprisoned for four days, during which time he freely admitted to police examiners the occurrence as described above. By court order he was released on bond for a psychiatric examination.

Family History

E W haltingly describes his father as a hard-working but remote, strict, and arbitrary person with little warmth or understanding in his family relationships. The mother is characterized as more "kindly," although temperamental and rigid in her prejudices. The older brother (now 30) is overbearing, and since his return from service has become increasingly alcoholic and physically abusive.

Personal History

E W was born in Chicago to a life handicapped by financial privation and familial strife. He was retarded in school, and developed feelings of general inadequacy and isolation. He quit 9th grade to work at a minor postal job for a year and then, after misstating his age, succeeded in enlisting for army service. He adapted well to the regularity and security of army life, and would have remained in it except for his mother's pleas that she was ill and needed him at home. After his return he held a succession of jobs only briefly, quitting or being fired because the proficiencies required, other than driving a bus, exceeded his abilities. Similarly, he has found it difficult to cultivate interests and friendships, and has remained isolated and lonesome. He therefore wanted to return to the army as the only place where he was needed and useful, but felt deterred by his mother's continued insistence that he stay at home and protect her from her unpredictable husband and older son.

Sexual History

E W's sexual development was also severely limited: aside from occasional masturbation, he had no sexual experiences until two frustrating contacts with prostitutes during his army service. On one occasion, he had also submitted to mutual masturbation with a "service buddy" when both were partially intoxicated, but had no other experiences until the incident on the bus. He stated that he would greatly prefer "to be with girls, except I don't have any money, and they don't think I'm very smart"; nevertheless, he hopes a 17-year-old waitress he now knows will marry him when she comes of age "so we can settle down and have our own home away from our families."

Psychologic

E W's limited capacities for abstraction, logic, memory, and other intellectual functions indicate only a borderline intelligence, with social skills relatively underdeveloped. However, he is sincere, frank, friendly, and, although socially handicapped and naive, is devoid of antagonisms or aggressions in any way vicious or dangerous.

Impression

Immature personality; homosexual tendencies are not of pathologic intensity and would subside under favorable circumstances.

Interview with E W's Mother

Confirms in general the above data and inferences. Mrs. W stated that she is now willing to let her son reenlist if so advised.

Summary

E W is an experientially-deprived and intellectually- and culturally-limited individual subject to minor deviations of behavior under special circumstances, but capable of fair adaptations to a supervised milieu, such as in peacetime military service. In the past, and in his preceding nine months as a school bus driver he had exhibited no proclivities toward serious aberrations; however, he might be disturbed in this regard under the homosexual stresses of a prison environment. An alternative would be directive counselling under supervised parole.

Follow-Up

E W was placed on six months of closely supervised probation on a municipal work project, a verdict that kept him out of prison and satisfied both families. At the end of this period E W found more suitable work as a condominium janitor, and reported all well. An examination of the boy as directed by the court likewise indicated that he had retained no elicitable adverse effects from the episode. (JHM)

Case 15. Sexual Abuse with Indications for Court Action

With regard to a request by a judge for counsel in a divorce action, the potential mistreatment of minors required appropriate recommendations.

Report to the Honorable _____

Anamnesis, Mrs. W

Mrs. W's descriptions of her difficulties were so confused and contradictory that, as here summarized, they can be regarded as mainly significant of her disturbed mental state.

Mrs. W idealizes her father (to whose memory she is still exceedingly attached) as "perfect in every way," whereas her mother is described in highly critical terms. She admits that she herself was always "high-strung," but managed to complete college and engage in substitute teaching. After dating many men, she "fell in love with one who I thought was much like my father ... but when he propositioned me and didn't have father's perfect integrity ... I decided to go to Nevada with him ... he had a nervous breakdown, but I thought he had pernicious anemia like my father so I married him. For a long time my other boyfriends shadowed him and my brother threatened to kill him because they were so jealous."

Marital History. In effect, Mrs. W describes her sexual relations with her husband as consisting of bizarre variations until their son, K, was four, after which Mr. W preferred pederasty with the child. She repeatedly heard K screaming while locked in the bathroom with his father; however, she made no attempt to interfere until K was 13, when a school doctor reported that K was being sexually abused. She then accused her husband of homosexuality *elsewhere,* separated from him, went "back to teaching," and now wants a divorce.

Psychologic Appraisal. Scattered through these recollections were vague admissions that she herself had had several "nervous breakdowns" requiring hospitalizations. Her ideation is currently diffuse, repetitious, and fantasy-ridden. For example, she states that her four former divorce lawyers, each of whom she dismissed in turn, have now formed a cabal to influence the court's judgment against her, and that her present attorney has also warned her that I may be similarly bribed. Her present plans are (a) to secure a divorce and alimony, (b) to teach K about sex by "showing him (sic) examples," and (c) to expand a "nondirective school for children" she had recently established from its present enrollment of four tots, ages two to five, to an indefinite member at various ages.

Anamnesis of Mr. W

Mr. W's mother died when Mr. W was nine, after which his father, a minister, initiated frequent homosexual relations with the boy, which continued sporadically until the father's death last autumn. Mr. W grew to be a dependent, retiring, ineffectual individual who achieved barely marginal school, occupational, and social adaptations. Soon after marriage at 30 he decided he did not love Mrs. W because she "kept beating K as a baby because he was so dumb ... she had crazy interests ... and probably screwed around." He did not object to "keep things quiet," but when she finally accused him of "being a queer" a year ago, he first offered "to take a lie test if she would pay for it," and then, when she refused, he "told her I had a right to kill her" and left home to live with a male cousin. After the divorce, "K will be placed in some foster home five days a week so I can have him weekends."

Psychologic Appraisal. Mr. W exhibits low average intelligence, retarded and deviant ideation, inappropriate affect and defective insight. My examination could not directly elicit that he had actually practiced pederasty, but did reveal strong indications of retained homosexual patterns. In any case, Mr. W seems poorly equipped to look after his own or his son's best interests.

K W, 11

K, painfully shy and inarticulate, responded hesitantly and vaguely to inquiries. Gently pressed, he described various oral and anal contacts with his father, but expressed little resentment. Mom was sometimes "mean but OK," so he "would go with either Mom or Pop."

Psychologic. K is currently still retarded in 4th grade. As inferred from his limited knowledge and vocabulary, poverty of ideation, difficulties in abstraction and judgment, and his performance on elementary paper and pencil tests, his IQ was judged to be in the mid-70s.

Physical. Findings were suggestive of hypothyroidism, to be confirmed by laboratory tests.

Recommendations

Divorce between Mr. and Mrs. W seems desirable; however, neither parent is sufficiently competent or rational to be entrusted with their son K. Instead, the boy needs an extended residency at an adolescent treatment facility such as a juvenile institute followed by a suitable foster home placement.

An urgent issue is presented by Mrs. W's management of a children's "day school," a responsibility for which she is characterologically ill-suited. I therefore respectfully request the Court to take this issue, as will her allegations of father-son incest under judicial advisement.

Follow-Up

The divorce was granted, but Mrs. W was constrained by the court from opening any school for minor children. However, due to legal technicalities no action was taken in regards to Mr. W other than to remand K to an institution for retarded adolescents from which visitation rights to either parent could be strictly controlled. (JHM)

Case 16. When the Future of the Children is a Primary Concern

Report to the Presiding Judge, Court of Domestic Relations

Purpose of the Examination

As part of a recent divorce decree, Mrs. N was awarded custody of the couple's youngest child, L, a girl, age 10. To complete the settlement, the present consultation was requested by the Court as to the best future for the middle sons, To, 11, and Th, 15; D, 17, is in military service.

Procedure

To assure adequate data and optimal appraisal, Mr. and Mrs. N were interviewed jointly on May 5th, individually on May 13th, and To and Th together and separately on May 17th. Each interview lasted about an hour.

Mr. B N

Personal History. Mr. N, 44, was apparently overindulged and excessively protected by both his parents in childhood and, though outgoing and sociable throughout youth, seems never to have developed a sensitivity for, and adaptability to, the adverse attitudes and opinions of others. Nevertheless, he graduated from technical school, has helped manage his elder brother's business, and has become moderately secure financially. After little heterosexual experience he married G at 26, mainly because she "was young and jovial." Once G was "secured" however, he again shifted his interests to his own family and hobbies, and remained unaware of her growing resentments, as evidenced by their increasingly frequent quarrels, her insistence on twin beds and her announcement two years ago that she was having and would continue to have extramarital relations. In turn, he admits to having "drunk regularly for years . . . sometimes losing my temper with G and beating her up" and having once "shook her up when she came home after making passes at everybody at a party and then screwing another man"—yet he "could never see why G should ever be unhappy with me or what she was complaining about." Even now, he "would have her back for the sake of the home and the children."

Mental Status. Mr. N has average intellectual capacities but lacks general information, imagery, abstract and symbolic thought, and speed and flexibility of judgment. Dynamically, he is insufficiently emancipated from maternal dependence, and much of his professed "tolerance" of his wife's behavior springs from his need for her as a maternal surrogate. Preemptive also is his desire for custody of his middle sons as an indirect way of "keeping some influence on my family." Fortunately, he is marginally aware of his personality difficulties and professes to be willing to seek psychiatric help for them.

Mrs. G N, Age 38

Personal History. Mrs. N's father committed suicide during her first year of life, after which she was raised by her mother, "always proper, and dignified." She states that because she "always felt lonely," soon after graduating high school she married B who "seemed to be an older man with a good education and a steady income." However, although she "continued to love him until a year ago," she almost immediately grew dissatisfied with his alcoholism, his insistence that his mother live with them, his excessive permissiveness with or violent attacks on the children, and his complete sexual indifference after her hysterectomy for uterine tumors five years ago. Since she was "assured by B's doctor" (sic?) that this was willfull rather than organic, she resorted to extramarital relations "to restore my self-respect as a woman," and then, (sic?) "on the advice of [my] priest" decided to shock her husband into greater attentiveness by telling him about her sexual affairs. Instead, he accused her of "being a whore in front of the children," allegedly became even more neglectful, insulting, contrary, and violent in his conduct until she "hit him with divorce papers a year ago." After this he acted "more human," but then it was "too late" (all quotations hers). She now intends to support herself and continue her extramarital adventures although she has no present intention to remarry.

Mental Status. Mrs. N has an alert intelligence, a friendly, interested, cooperative, and somewhat flirtatious manner and a partially defiant frankness about her attitudes and actions. Her feelings toward her ex-husband are now almost wholly those of derision, contempt, and abhorrence, so that a reconciliation or even any concessions on her part not to her immediate interests are excluded. However, she admits that, although Th and To "are wonderful boys, they may want to go with Mr. N because he can give them more money and lets them get away with anything; and if they do he can have them, if I get decent visiting rights."

Th, 15

A fairly thorough examination indicated that despite his mother's evasively recounted sexual peculiarities and obviously overstimulating behavior (e.g., parading nude at home, erotic telephone calls), Th had dealt with the increasing sexual strife and physical turmoil to which he had been subjected by denying its importance and trying to maintain his allegiance to both parents. In accord with this posture, he has "nothing against either Mom or Pop—I think they both exaggerate against each other," but currently prefers to go with his father "only because it would be tougher on Mom to support us." He anticipates that living temporarily with an uncle will be fairly pleasant, "until Dad buys a two-flat and moves Grandma in with us or hires a housekeeper, and has Uncle P and his family live upstairs." He would "like to see Mom every month or so" until he goes to college "to become (sic) a medical illustrator."

As indicated, Th assumes an attitude of poised maturity beyond his age, hiding deep affects and resentments that may break through later in life. Should that cause difficulties, early counseling and guidance would be helpful, but this does not appear to be practicable now.

To, 11

To, although less perceptive and orientated, also believes he would be better off for the time being living with his "Dad and Uncle and my cousins M and D, and see Mom sometimes."

Recommendations

It may be well, in view of Mrs. N's disturbed conduct, to have fairly regular reports to the court as to whether the girl L is receiving proper care and guidance in her mother's custody. As to the questions with regard to Th and To, the following considerations apply:

(a) Mrs. N will not soon have available either the financial means or the environmental setting for raising them with proper example and discipline unless she marries a man capable of being an especially devoted and competent stepfather.

(b) In contrast, Mr. N states that he can furnish them with adequate care, companionship, and guidance in the home of his younger brother, where they would be protected from premature libidinal stimulation and would have the stability, serenity, and familial and peer relationships they require. Visits to their mother should be continued until gradual emancipation, but should be limited or discontinued if their father or uncle reports that either boy is distrubed by them. It would also be well if Mr. N were instructed, for his children's sake as well as his own, to seek psychiatric counsel as to his own behavior. (JHM)

Chapter 12

REVIEW AND INTEGRATION

Adolescence is a period of rapid and definitive development of an individual's unique personality. Puberty confers a capacity to perpetuate our race and, through later parental and social guidance, determine its future. This book explored the essential role of sexuality in this cyclic progression.

In brief, Chapter 1 reviewed the emergence of sexuality from the beginning of time to the most complex product of evolution: human beings.

Chapter 2 examined the embryonic phylogenetic determinants of sexuality, as also profoundly affected by the neonate's initial respiratory, tactile, and visual experiences. The "narcissistic, oral, anal, phallic, Oedipal, and latent phases of erotic development" through childhood and adolescence were reformulated.

Chapter 3 surveyed the actual expressions of sexuality before, during, and after puberty, as again greatly modified by gender and cultural norms.

Chapter 4 specified the urgent (Ur) needs of human beings: physical health, interpersonal securities, and comforting faiths. The chapter then explored the deviations in sexually-related behavior during adolescence in response to family dissensions, poverty, abuse, defects in education, social injustices, and misuse of drugs, with attendant personality disintegrations.

Chapter 5 questioned the current system of classifying juvenile disorders, and redefined "diagnosis" as comprising a judicious assessment of the genetic, somatic, and past and recent experiential determinants of adolescent conduct as relevant to the modes of environmental, medical, individual, familial, and social therapies for various forms of deviance, and the prospects (prognosis) for personal and cultural readaptations.

Chapter 6 elaborated the fundamental (Ur) aspirations of human beings for the somatic vitality, social security, and comforting beliefs outlined in Chapter 4, and described research indicating that, to be effective, any form of treatment must alleviate corresponding Ur anxieties over physical illnesses, interpersonal alienations, and/or transgressions of essential faiths. The therapeutic modalities especially applicable to adolescents were then reviewed under the headings of (1) the prestige of the therapist, (2) the enhancement of rapport, (3) the clarification of past and current pathogenic stresses, (4) the relief of symptoms, (5) the reeducation and resocialization of the patient and his or her mentors, and (6) the reutilization of these clinical vectors until (7) reasonably stable and satisfactory personal and social rehabilitation has been achieved.

Chapter 7 discussed in detail the medical, familial, and juristic cautions that should be exercised in counselling adolescents as to the emotional relationships, erotic techniques, contraceptive precautions, dangers of assault and pregnancy, covert attempts at abortion, and other serious complications of adolescent sexuality.

Chapter 8 distinguished the parent-child or intersibling traumata of incest from its often more damaging social and legal complications.

Chapter 9 explored the devastating effects of the misuse of drugs on sex-related behavior, and the individual and global measures to be taken to prevent the attendant illiteracy, vagrancy, violence, crime, prostitution, and personality deteriorations affecting increasing numbers of our youth.

Chapter 10 considered the tragedies of sexually-related adolescent suicides, their causes and modes of prevention, and the treatment of threatened or bereaved families.

Precis

A principle theme throughout the text and case illustrations has been that adolescent sexuality can be best understood in the context of associated "normal" and deviant patterns of behavior, all of which are contingent not only on individual genetic and developmental factors, but are also responsive to economic and other social stresses such as the imminence of nuclear genocide. The authors therefore trust that all who read this book, whether a troubled adolescent, a concerned parent, teacher, social worker, or other mental health professional, a jurist, and especially a futuristically-oriented political leader, will have been guided not only as to the protean causes, manifestations, and treatment of teenage sexual and related deviations of conduct, but will also join in providing a more rational, secure and humane world for our youth and their offspring.

RECOMMENDED READING

Chess, S. and Thomas, A.: *Origin and Evolution of Behavior Disorders.* New York, Brunner/Mazel, 1984.

Masserman, J.H.: *The Biodynamic Roots of Human Behavior.* Springfield, Illinois, Charles C Thomas, 1968.

Masserman, J.H. (Ed.): *Youth: A Transcultural Approach.* New York, Grune and Stratton, 1969.

Masserman, J.H. (Ed.): *Man for Humanity.* Springfield, Illinois, Charles C Thomas, 1972.

Masserman, J.H. (Ed.): *Current Psychiatric Therapies.* New York, Grune and Stratton, 1986, vol. 23.

Paulson, D. (Ed.): *Voices of Survival.* Santa Barbara, California, Capra Press, 1986.

NAME INDEX

A

Adler, A., 17
American Psychiatric Association, 32
A.P.A. Commission on Psychiatric Therapies,
    39, 56

B

Bonaparte, M., 18
Braceland, F.J., 32

C

Caesar, 25
Calderone, M., 44
Camus, A., 17
Chess, S., 95
Comte, A., 29, 32
Courtois, C.A., 49
Cullen, W., 30
Czikzentmihaly, M., 39

D

Demosthenes, 25
Durkheim, E., 61
Dylens, J.W., 56

E

Erickson, E.H., 18
Erhardt, K., 24
Erman, A.H., 24
Esman, A.H., 28

F

Ferenczi, S., 16, 17

Finkelhor, D., 49
Fishman, E.C., 39
Frank, J., 20, 30
Freedman, A.M., 28, 39, 43, 44
Freud, A., 18
Freud, S., 9–16, 18, 49
Furman, E., 18

G

Giovacchini, P., 39
Goodman, J.M., 24
Greenspan, S.I., 18

H

Haim, A., 61
Hawkins, S.W., 7, 25
Hegeler, I., 44
Hegeler, S., 44
Henderson, J., 49
Hersen, M., 32
Holmes, D., 43, 44
Homer, 25
Horney, K., 17, 18
Husserl, 17

I

Illinois Department of Substance Abuse, 56

J

Jastrow, P., 7
Jensen, G.D., 24
Johnson, V., 43, 44
Jung, K., 29

97

SUBJECT INDEX

A

Abnormalities, 5
  sexual, 6
Abortion, 24
Addicts Anonymous, 55
Addictions, 6, 27, 37, 53
Adolescence, 93
  future, 94
AIDS, 23, 24, 42
Alcoholics Anonymous, 49
Alcoholism, 51
  experimental, 55
Alienation, 58
Amicus curiae, 48
Anamnesis, 33, 35, 38
Anomie, 60
Anorexia nervosa, 11
Antabuse, 51
Anxiety, 41
  separation, 74
  sexual, 41
Arson, 82
Athletics, 13
Audy Home, 82
Autism, 5

B

Barbiturate, 54
Behavior,
  adaptive, 25
  deviant, 14
  maladaptive, 26
Birth sensations, 9
Birth trauma, 17
Bonding, 10
Bulimia, 11

C

Castration, 68
  anxiety, 14
Character formation, 14
Child, abuse, 85
  care, 88
Chromosomes, 4
Clitoris, 12
Cloning, 3, 7
Cocaine, 53
Codeine, 54
Coitus, 13
  adolescent, 19
  dysfunction, 66
  vectors, 19
Condoms, 23
Confidentiality, 35, 64
Consultations, 63
Contentment, 58
Contraception, 20
Cosa Nostra, 27
Counselling, 41
  parents, 43
Countertransference, 35
Crack, 27, 53
Crime, cartels,
Cunnilingus, 11, 66
Cyclazocine, 54
Cystic fybrosis, 6, 58

D

Darvon, 54
Demerol, 54
Delerium tremens, 52
Delinquency, sexual, 75
Delusions, 14, 52
Depressions, 17, 65

99